MEET MY MEDICAL DIRECTOR

MEET *My* MEDICAL DIRECTOR

Navigating Cancer's Storm

LISA ENGELMAN

PARAKALEO
PRESS

Published by Parakaleo Press

Printed in the United States of America

ISBN-13 (trade paper): 978-1-7328265-0-2

Unless otherwise noted, Scripture quotations are from the Holy Bible,
English Standard Version,® © 2001 by Crossway Bibles, a publishing ministry of
Good News Publishers. Used by permission. All rights reserved.

Scripture quotations marked NIV are from the Holy Bible,
New International Version,® NIV,® © 1973, 1978, 1984, 2011 by Biblica, Inc.™
Used by permission. All rights reserved worldwide.

Scripture quotations marked NLT are from the Holy Bible, New Living Translation,
© 1996, 2004, 2007 by Tyndale House Foundation. Used by permission of Tyndale
House Publishers, Inc., Carol Stream, Illinois 60188. All rights reserved.

Italics in Scripture quotations are the emphasis of the author.

Editing by Rebecca Lawson, GladBooks.net
Cover and interior design by Rob Williams, InsideOutCreativeArts.com

PIOH is a registered trademark of White Heron.

This book is not intended to be a substitute for the medical advice of a licensed physician.
Readers should consult with their doctors in any matters relating to their health.

TO JESUS—

MY BREATH AND MY VICTORY

CONTENTS

Foreword

By Pastor Jerry Rueb

Suffering is the gift that nobody wants. But every believer needs suffering if he or she wants to know God intimately. Don't get me wrong. I'm not suggesting that we should seek to suffer, for that would only be replacing one misconception for another. This side of heaven, we don't need to search for trials and heartaches. But they inevitably find us, because God has actually ordained them for higher purposes: "It has been *granted* to you that for the sake of Christ you should not only believe in him but also suffer for his sake" (Phil. 1:29). These words echo off the stone dungeon walls of the dark and damp cell in which the apostle Paul lived two thousand years ago. From the confines of his intense and unexplained suffering, Paul taught us in counterintuitive ways, calling suffering a *charisma*—a grace gift from God. Imagine that! Some of God's greatest gifts are wrapped in tears and sorrow.

From the time I met Lisa Engelman and her family, I knew that God was gifting her with something powerful to say to fellow believers. Lisa's ability to describe the journey of suffering impressed me as a gift from God. Her pain is as real as anyone who has been diagnosed with cancer can experience. Her questions and searching for answers go as deep as those of anyone I know. The weight of her being Steve's young wife and the mother of their four little children wraps her story with intensity and powerful emotions. But the greatest gift that Lisa offers fellow travelers along the road of suffering is a fresh vision of Jesus—her Medical Director.

We who follow Jesus must remember that He did not exempt Himself from the most excruciating suffering. Isaiah predicted that Jesus willingly went to the cross and "was pierced for our transgressions; he was crushed for our iniquities; upon him was the chastisement that brought us peace, and with his wounds we are healed" (Isa. 53:5). Jesus looked through His suffering and found joy, knowing that it would bring us the gift of everlasting life.

So as you read this book, join Lisa as she charts the path through the dark valleys of suffering into the glorious light and freedom of following the crucified and risen Savior, Jesus Christ.

Preface

Suffering surrounds us. It invades countries, cities, homes, hearts, minds and bodies and wreaks havoc, whether from war or hurricanes or job loss or relational conflict—or the little cell of the human body turning malignant.

I unwrapped cancer for Christmas in 2013. That doesn't make me special. Cancer has become grievously common. This is not a cancer-cure book. It's not a case for choosing alternative cancer care over conventional cancer care, though you will catch glimpses of where Jesus has led me in my own cancer journey. Jesus has taken me to the chemo room, to a clinic in Mexico, and to integrative medical centers.

This is the story of a Savior and a girl who needed to be rescued. When I was drowning in fear and confusion, Jesus reached out His hand to take hold of mine and lead me through the storm. It's a story of love—God's love. It's a story of light—Jesus speaking light into my darkness. It's a story of how Jesus has directed me through the maze of cancer treatment decisions as a momma with four itty bitty children. It's a chronicle of His many whispers to me along the way, saying, "This is the way, walk in it" (Isa. 30:21).

The Bible was written "for our instruction, that through endurance and through the encouragement of the Scriptures we might have hope" (Rom. 15:4). The Old Testament story of King Asa is no exception. I learned something vital from King Asa's mistake of seeking help only from physicians and forgetting to seek God first: "In the thirty-ninth year of his reign Asa was diseased in his feet, and his disease became severe. Yet even in his disease he did not seek the LORD, but sought help from physicians. And Asa slept with his fathers, dying in the forty-first year of his reign" (2 Chron. 16:12–13).

One day I cried out to my husband, "I have no one to help me. We can go to multiple healthcare professionals, but no one has the answer for *me*."

Jesus whispered to my heart, "Ask *Me*. Let *Me* guide you, daughter. Trust in Me with all your heart; do not lean on your own understanding. In all your ways come to Me, and I will direct your paths" (see Prov. 3:5–6).

I got on my knees that day and asked Jesus to be my Medical Director. To guide me. To help me trust and obey Him, no matter what He asked me to do. To walk by faith and not by sight. To trust that He would bring my life to its intended completion (see Phil. 1:6). Since that day Jesus has directed me through turbulent waters of decision making. He has also set me free from the fear of death and enveloped me with His light, truth, and love.

My entire cancer journey is tucked away throughout the chapters of this book. God's sustaining grace, gentle shepherding, and miraculous provision adorn these pages. I have included journal entries, blog posts filled with unedited emotion, nourishing Scripture, sneak peeks into the hearts of my husband and children, and my "top twenty-five" home-based cancer weapons list.

When you or someone you love is faced with a cancer diagnosis, and fear freezes right thinking, it is my hope that you will be drawn into a union with Jesus that enables you to say no to fear and yes to His love—His perfect love that grounds us in His promises.

Jesus made wildflowers to bloom in my wilderness. As you read of those wildflowers throughout this book, may they delight your palate, for they are sweet to the soul and healing to the bones. May you be strengthened by knowing that every cell of your body and each mountain of impossibility are under God's authority. Oh, taste and see the Lord's goodness both in your valleys and on your mountaintops!

When the clock stood still for me at 3:35 a.m. on November 25, 2013, Jesus held out His Savior hand, beckoning me to walk on water with trust and obedience. Gazing upon me with eyes of love, His whisper traveled across the stormy sea: "I am the Lord your Healer. Will you trust Me?" (see Exod. 15:26).

So come on in—meet my Medical Director, my Healer: Jesus, the sweetest name I know.

In Gratitude

To my husband, Stephen Engelman, who likes to go by "just husband," being your wife is the greatest earthly gift bestowed on me. Our love is a gift from the One who *is* love. Steadfast, tender, selfless, devoted as husband and daddy. King of juice, barista, and chef. My lineman and my comrade. Whatever God calls you to, you are all in. Our God has seen your every act of selfless love. Great is your reward. Our God will be waiting with arms open wide to receive His son and His servant into perfect rest. Oh, the joy it will be to hear Him speak the words I know are coming: "Well done, Steve, well done!" I love you into eternity. Grassy meadows await us!

To Luke, Ellie, Gracie, and Sammy J, I *love* being your momma. Thank you for every giggle we share, all our hide-and-seek games, the slow pajama mornings, the bedtime stories, your big morning hugs, and most of all, how you point me to Jesus. You are so quick to forgive. I love your questions, your thoughts on heaven, and the way you use your gifts for Jesus. If I could line up a million kids and choose four, I would choose you every time. I love you forever and always.

To Daddy and Momma, because of you I was introduced to Jesus at a young age and raised to love Him. Daddy, thank you for the countless days you spent making your own food and sharing Momma with me. Momma, you have been my rescue over and over, the glue for my family for so many of the cancer years. From caring for the children to packing up our house to helping with this manuscript—thank you! Daddy and Momma, you hold a special forever place in this girl's heart. I love you! I am so glad God gave me you.

To my Grandpa, Reverend Mark L. Mitchell, your love for the Word is what I think about when excitement over a passage in Scripture takes over me. You used your Bible to preach but never needed to look at it. It was hidden in your heart and found its way into your incredible stories. One day I will be in the arms of Jesus. After His big hug, I will look over His shoulder and see you with a huge smile of celebration on your face. We will have a lot of stories to catch up on. And maybe, just maybe, we can sit under an apple tree.

To Dr. Vanessa Lyon, Dirk Yow, Grace Kerr, Dr. Chelsea Markus Hauswirth, Dr. Cassie Herbst, Dr. Tony and Marcy Jimenez, Dr. Curiel, and my Hope4Cancer family, to you I have never been a statistic. You saw my heart. Your kindness and compassion have been sweet to my soul and healing to my bones. Thank you for walking with me.

To Pastor Jerry and Sue Rueb, your enduring passion for Jesus and His Word shines steady hope into weary hearts. Our Lord's energy is powerfully at work in and through you both. Thank you for introducing me to Becky and for encouraging me to write. I see Jesus in you both. The kingdom feast awaits!

To Becky and Steve Lawson, God sent you. Becky, tears fell when I saw the beautifully edited manuscript. Your attention to detail combined with your gentle approach gave us an enjoyable first publishing experience. Thank you to Steve Lawson for your expertise and insight—you and Becky are an amazing team. You came alongside a family that needed some extra care and grace in traveling through this publishing journey. Thank you for being His love to us.

To Rob Williams, your design for the cover and interior of this book fully embodies the journey this has been. When we saw it, it took our breath away. Thank you for using your gifts for our King.

To Jennifer Cullis, you have an amazing gift for language and a keen eye for detail. As you searched this book for errors, you put yourself into our story and walked it with us. You didn't just read the words; you experienced them. Thank you for sharing in our journey through your proofreading of this book.

To my faces of grace, you have snuggled my littles and nurtured their hearts. Your door has been open for my children to come for playdates and taste a bit of normal. You helped with fundraisers, offered transportation, and invited the kids on field trips. You have given financially. You have persevered in prayer over me and my family. You are a listening ear, a safe place to come and share my heart. You are my spiritual mentors. You are my voices of encouragement. All has been grace. Thank you!

To my triune God, Papa, my tender Arms; Jesus, my Beloved; Spirit, my Whisper. You turned my darkness to light. My story is Your story. Let me live it well.

PART 1

An Unexpected Path

Fear Factor:
The Diagnosis

At 3:35 a.m. on November 25, 2013, the concept of my mortality sprang into stark reality for me.

Sudden abdominal pain on a November evening drove me to the emergency room. Earlier that day I had called my primary-care physician; she had suggested that I get imaging to look for gallstones.

With my children's bedtime approaching, my sister Laurie came over to watch five-year-old Luke, three-year-old Ellie, and one-year-old Gracie at our home. My husband, Steve, and I brought our four-month-old baby, Sammy J, to the hospital with us so I could nurse him and keep him close.

We went through the usual ER waiting and triage process. By midnight the staff was wheeling me off to an ultrasound. It took the technician all of one minute to stop the ultrasound and get a doctor, who promptly ordered a CT scan. I had no idea what a CT scan was, so I wasn't aware that I should have been concerned.

After the scan I was back in the ER room, where, unbeknownst to me, I experienced my first of many waiting-for-results experiences. My six-foot-five husband attempted to fold himself into a chair next to my bed that looked to be a good fit for my five-year-old son. He nodded off to sleep at three in the morning with his head warming my shoulder.

The ticking of the clock kept me company as my thoughts wandered. *How long does it take to diagnose gallstones?* I was confident in my primary-care physician's theory about gallstones being the source of my pain. There was a simple explanation for everything.

Before dawn shed its first light, two doctors came into my room, looked me in the eyes, and said, "I'm sorry to say that we think you have cancer. We need to admit you immediately for further testing. Do you have any questions?"

Questions? Yes, a lot of them. The first being, am I going to die?

I didn't ask that question. I didn't ask any questions at all. My voice box had been paralyzed by the C word. My heart raced. Being propped up in a bed didn't stop dizziness from making the room turn circles. Steve looked up with sleepy eyes that said, *Surely I am still asleep. They did not just say that my wife has cancer.*

We instantly locked eyes on our sweet baby snuggly tucked into his car seat, fast asleep. He was so little. So little to be instantly separated from me. But neither Steve nor Sammy J could stay the night. Visiting hours were over, and our other children needed attending to. My husband and baby went home for the night.

The hospital staff moved me upstairs into a room with an angry cancer patient. I had a curtained-off space large enough for a bed and a whiteboard on the wall above me. The doctor had written "LYMPHOMA" in huge capital red letters on the whiteboard. I didn't know much about lymphoma, but I knew in that moment that I didn't like the word. I was afraid to know what it meant for me, my husband, and my children.

Facing Fear

Fear cripples. When the fog of fear settles in, we lose our ability to think clearly and wait patiently. Fear dulls our capacity to give and receive love. Fear lies, steals, and seeks to destroy perspective and joy.

I tasted cold, dark fear during Thanksgiving of 2013 in my curtained-off space in that hospital room. I found reprieve in certain moments when the Spirit brought scriptures embedded deep in my soul to soothe my confusion. I waited three long hours with Jesus by my side, watching the clock tick. My body, filling up with milk, yearning for my baby, Sammy, echoed the growing plea in my heart for my husband to return.

The first face that appeared in my room as the dawn rescued me was that of a friendly resident doctor. She picked up a marker and wrote "possible" in front of the word "LYMPHOMA" that the previous doctor had written on the whiteboard. She declared that no one was going to diagnose me without proper biopsies and testing. She was my new favorite doctor! Her name was Faith.

I breathed out relief when Steve returned with Sammy J for me to nurse him. I buried my face in Sammy's rolls of chub, comforted by his nearness. Happiness traveled with Sammy J wherever he went. I felt even better when I was moved to my own hospital room. Steve and I now had a private spot to snuggle with Sammy J and receive the visitors who began sprinkling in.

A team of doctors waltzed into my room the second day of my hospital stay. This friendly infectious-disease team surrounded my bed, firing crazy questions about where I had lived in my life. I liked them because they were looking for a quirky virus rather than cancer. If they struck gold, we could erase "LYMPHOMA" from the whiteboard and from my life.

My heart took to pounding out of control each time the doctors' shoes clicked ominously toward my hospital room. Each time it was another test, another waiting period, and more silence. Silence can be so loud. I was discharged without a conclusion. Next up would be another biopsy and a PET scan, just in time for the Christmas season.

Waiting

Time crawled over the next four weeks as Steve and I slowly inched our feet, one after the other, toward the tasks at hand. Meeting the needs of our children kept us moving forward. The crowds seemed to run over us on our attempts to get groceries. Had people always gone that fast? I watched in awe as shoppers moved quickly through their grocery lists, while I tried to remember why I had come. Things that had been so easy a couple weeks ago became grueling marathon events. The store lights cast gloomy shadows over the aisles. I felt half present. I often left with empty hands and a mind taken over by intruding thoughts—pictures of what Steve would do without me at his side, my little ones without their momma to be their biggest cheerleader. Thoughts can suffocate.

When my firstborn was a baby, I had started a small family blog in lieu of social media. It was a place for family and friends to see pictures of our growing family and hear about our happenings. Little did I know that five years into my blog, cancer would find its way into it:

My lens that I see my family and the world with has been changed forever. One of my greatest sources of anxiety in

24

my life has been losing someone I love who is very close to me. I agonized the days when we were awaiting to find out if Ellie Joy had leukemia or, ironically, lymphoma when she was a toddler. I would worry when Steve would go out on a bike ride and be late returning home, or when he would get on a plane for a business trip. I have held too tightly to what is not mine to hold on to. I think it took walking through one of my greatest fears to know that, as a Christian, I have nothing to fear. (blog post, November 30, 2013)

The call I received on December 23, 2013, shocked me, but it did not surprise God. He had known that this phone call would be coming before I was ever born. Two days before Christmas, at the age of thirty-five, as wife to one superb husband and mother to four children ages five and under, I was officially diagnosed with early stage-three follicular non-Hodgkin's lymphoma (FNHL), a slow-growing form of lymphoma. FNHL is defined by Western medicine as a treatable, but not curable, disease.

Faced with Options

Two days after my diagnosis, I wrote,

I can't do this alone. God as my anchor, Steve in the trenches with me, my family, my beloved friends, I need all of you to pick me up when I'm down. To gently whisper His truths to me, to love my kids even when they are not acting so lovable in their kid moments, and to encourage Steve along the journey too. I trust the Lord to help me trust Him when I have my faltering moments, as there have been many in just forty-eight hours. (blog post, December 25, 2013)

Fear freezes right thinking in its tracks. Oncologists presented us with options that had me on the fast track to more biopsies and aggressive treatments. Their words sent waves of fear ripping through me: "Do this now, or you will die from cancer. And if you do it, you will still die from this cancer. But don't worry, we hope to have another treatment available to you by the time you use up these five treatments that we have available right now." The advice presented to me was to be sure to play my cards right.

The statistics regarding the trajectory of my earthly life closed in on me in one small office as we got up to leave. I passed by a crowded waiting room, wondering how many others were about to have the ground quake beneath their feet.

Steve and I began discussing treatment options. Neither of us felt that aggressive chemo for a cancer that was considered incurable was the path of wisdom. But what *was* the right path? We began to earnestly pray for clarity from God, to have our doubts removed, for Him to light up the way He wanted us to travel.

It helped us to visualize Jesus as our unchanging North Star. Just as sailors used the fixed position of the North Star to guide them to their destinations, Steve and I could trust Jesus and His unchanging Word to light the way through our night skies.

Are we making our medical decisions through prayer? Are we consulting our great Physician? Are we controlled by fear or by the Holy Spirit? Seeking first God's kingdom in all things is our joyous privilege as children of God. We can come before the Creator of the universe and ask Him to show us the way.

What if we asked *God* before we said yes to what a physician prescribes? What if we chose to trust Him to equip and provide for whatever medical path He calls us to? What if our healthcare treatment journeys were ordained by God before time began so more souls would come into His kingdom? So our paths would cross with believers who needed encouragement? So we could share the love of Jesus? So we would travel with the joy of Jesus filling our moments?

Steve and I decided early on that we did not want to be pressured by fearful opinions, statistics, or conventional wisdom. Instead we would lay the many options presented to us before Jesus and ask Him to lead us through the storm we faced called cancer.

No Need for Fear

All our days were ordained before one of them came to be (see Ps. 139:16). No circumstance in our lives will ever surprise Almighty God. Jesus Christ died on the cross for our sins, conquering death, setting us free from living enslaved to the fear of death (see Heb. 2:15). For those of us who have given our lives to Jesus and trusted Him as our Lord and Savior, death is our rich entrance into His kingdom (see 2 Pet. 1:11). It is our anticipation of meeting Jesus face to Face that will change the way we live today.

God is love. There is no fear in love. God has not given us a spirit of fear but of power, love, and self-discipline (see 2 Tim. 1:7). Giving our hearts to Jesus is the key to being set free from the fear of death. It is the single most important medical decision any human will ever make. Being God's child is our key to a peaceful medical journey, the perfect anti-aging medicine, and our guaranteed eternal cure for cancer.

What was the answer to the question that came to my mind with the ER doctor's cancer announcement, *Am I going to die?*

Yes. I am going to die. *But no doctor knows when.* Ecclesiastes 8:8 states, "As no one has power over the wind to contain it, so no one has power over the time of their death" (NIV). No doctor knows if I will die from cancer or if I will die from old age. The doctors are *not* in control. *God is.*

Until Jesus returns, we will all die. Some will go to eternal separation from God, and others will go to complete happiness with Jesus forever. In no way am I making light of death. When my husband was at his dad's side as his dad was going to meet Jesus, he sent me a message filled with gut-wrenching emotion: "I hate this . . . I hate this . . . I hate this . . . we are not supposed to be good at doing death." He wanted to ease his dad's pain. He wanted his dad to be able to communicate.

Death is gut-punching hard. Death was not God's original plan. But for the believer, death is turning a corner. When we round that corner, we will be met with joy unspeakable. For those of us left behind, death stings. We are here, and they are *there*. I have watched grief hit hard when precious friends whom I have met during my cancer journey have gone to be with Jesus. I long to ease the hurt of those left behind—to fill the aching hole.

When sadness, discouragement, or fear enters my heart, praying God's Word has been most soothing for me. My thoughts fade. His thoughts permeate my mind. Surpassing peace prevails.

Staying My Heart on Him

Amy Carmichael knew the secret of peace in times of storm: staying our hearts on Jesus:

> I am the God of the stars.
> They do not lose their way;
> Not one do I mislay.
> Their times are in My Hand;
> They move at My command.
>
> I am the God of the stars.
> Today, as yesterday,
> The God of thee and thine,

Less thine they are than Mine;
And shall Mine go astray?

I am the God of the stars.
Lift up thine eyes and see
As far as mortal may
Into Eternity;
And stay thy heart on Me.[1]

One night at the dinner table, several years into our cancer journey, I asked the children, "If you knew Jesus was coming back in two hours, what would you do right now?" With a huge smile, seven-year-old Ellie answered, "I'd watch out the window, and as soon as I saw Him, I would jump into His arms so He could carry me."

A huge grin burst from my heart onto my face. Thank You, Jesus, for being at work in my daughter and drawing her eyes up toward You.

As I imagined Ellie staring up into the night sky with happy eyes, watching and waiting for Jesus, I spontaneously started singing this stanza of Fanny Crosby's "Blessed Assurance":

Perfect submission, all is at rest
I in my Savior am happy and blessed
Watching and waiting, looking above
Filled with His goodness, lost in His love.

These powerful words came from a blind woman exercising her soul vision. We are surrounded by distractions that threaten to drop our focus from the cross to the screen. But the vision of our souls moves our feet by faith and not by sight (see 2 Cor. 5:7). As Fanny Crosby fixed the eyes of her soul on her beloved Savior, her song told a story of God's goodness and love.

He has given me a new song to sing, a hymn of praise to our God. Many will see what he has done and be amazed. They will put their trust in the LORD. Oh, the joys of those who trust the LORD, who have no confidence in the proud or in those who worship idols. O LORD my God, you have performed many wonders for us. Your plans for us are too numerous to list. You have no equal. If I tried to recite all your wonderful deeds, I would never come to the end of them. (Ps. 40:3–5, NLT)

When I wake up wrestling with life's emotional and physical struggles, God's Word speaks peace over the chaos in my heart. God's written promises and His Holy Spirit bring stillness of soul as I stay my heart on Him. He gives me a new song to sing: "The Lord is my shepherd; I have all that I need. He lets me rest in green meadows; he leads me beside peaceful streams. He renews my strength. He guides me along right paths, bringing honor to his name" (Ps. 23:1–3, NLT).

My young daughter is right—the safest way to eternity is in our Savior's arms!

Praying Scripture is a powerful weapon against fear, doubt, and discouragement. The voice of Jesus through His written Word and the power of the Holy Spirit puts fear on the run as we immerse ourselves in His precious words. The following scriptures are from a blog post I made in December 2013 entitled "God's Word to My Heart from the ER to Diagnosis." Let's pray! For we know that as we pray, *He* fights!

The LORD Your God is in your midst, a mighty one who will save; he will rejoice over you with gladness; he will quiet you by his love; he will exult over you with loud singing. (Zeph. 3:17)

The LORD God is a sun and shield; the LORD bestows favor and honor; no good thing does he withhold from those whose walk is blameless. LORD Almighty, blessed is the one who trusts in you. (Ps. 84:11–12, NIV)

Guard my life, for I am faithful to you; save your servant who trusts in you. You are my God; have mercy on me, Lord, for I call to you all day long. Bring *joy* to your servant, Lord, for I put my trust in you. (Ps. 86:2–4, NIV)

In the day of my trouble I will call upon you, for you answer me. (Ps. 86:7)

Do not fear, for I am with you; do not be dismayed, for I am your God. I will strengthen you and help you; I will uphold you with my righteous right hand. (Isa. 41:10, NIV)

The LORD is my strength and my shield; in him my heart trusts, and I am helped. (Ps. 28:7)

Because you are my help, I sing in the shadow of your wings. (Ps. 63:7, NIV)

You keep him in perfect peace whose mind is stayed on you, because he trusts in you. Trust in the LORD forever, for the LORD GOD is an everlasting rock. (Isa. 26:3–4)

As I was with Moses, so I will be with you. I will not leave you or forsake you. (Josh. 1:5)

Let the peace of Christ rule in your hearts, since as members of one body you were called to peace. And be thankful. (Col. 3:15, NIV)

Set your minds on things above, not on earthly things. (Col. 3:2, NIV)

Ah, Sovereign LORD, you have made the heavens and the earth by your great power and outstretched arm. *Nothing* is too hard for you. (Jer. 32:17, NIV)

The joy of the LORD is your strength. (Neh. 8:10)

A joyful heart is good medicine, but a crushed spirit dries up the bones. (Prov. 17:22)

The eternal God is your refuge, and underneath are the everlasting arms. (Deut. 33:27, NIV)

Let the beloved of the LORD rest secure in him, for he shields him all day long, and the one the LORD loves rests between his shoulders. (Deut. 33:12, NIV)

He gently leads those that have young. (Isa. 40:11, NIV)

Be strong in the Lord and in his mighty power. (Eph. 6:10, NIV)

Be strong and courageous and do the work. Do not be afraid or discouraged, for the LORD God, my God, is with you. (1 Chron. 28:20, NIV)

I have loved you with an everlasting love; I have drawn you with unfailing kindness. (Jer. 31:3, NIV)

Because of the LORD's great love we are not consumed, for his compassions never fail. They are new every morning; great is your faithfulness. (Lam. 3:22, NIV)

The law of the LORD is perfect, reviving the soul; . . . the precepts of the LORD are right, rejoicing the heart. The commandment of the LORD is pure, enlightening the eyes. (Ps. 19:7–8)

The word of the LORD is right and true; he is faithful in all he does. (Ps. 33:4, NIV)

[He] is able to do far more abundantly than all that we ask or think, according to the power at work within us. (Eph. 3:20)

May the God of hope fill you with all joy and peace as you trust in him, so that you may overflow with hope by the power of the Holy Spirit. (Rom. 15:13, NIV)

Our son Luke's life verse:

Nothing is impossible with God. (Luke 1:37, NLT)

Our daughter Ellie's life verse:

You make known to me the path of life; you will fill me with joy in your presence, with eternal pleasures at your right hand. (Ps. 16:11, NIV)

Our daughter Gracelyn's life verse:

God is able to make all grace abound to you, so that having all sufficiency in all things at all times, you may abound in every good work. (2 Cor. 9:8)

Our son Sammy J's life verse:

Be sure to fear the LORD and serve Him faithfully with all your heart; consider what great things He has done for you. (1 Sam. 12:24, NIV)

First Waves:
Seeking the Cure

The first waves of my cancer storm brought heightened awareness of the enemy's attacks, especially upon waking in the morning. For months after my cancer diagnosis, my first thought when waking was, *Is it real?* At every holiday or birthday the enemy's arrows flew at me faster. I fought wandering thoughts: *Is this my last Christmas? Will I be here for their next birthdays?*

The enemy loves to fling flaming arrows of fear, doubt, and discouragement at us. Satan is threatened by Christians who place their complete trust in Jesus Christ. Steve and I began to learn that when we were experiencing opposition from the enemy, it was confirmation that we were traveling in the right direction, right in step with God.

Voices, including ones from the Internet, bombarded us from all directions with well-meaning advice. Google is both friend and foe. The doctors advised a harsh chemotherapy combination of five drugs plus immunotherapy. This "one size fits all" approach was their standard of care. The problem is, there is just one uniquely created Lisa Engelman. I didn't fit into their box; numerous experiences in my life had proved my hyper-reactivity to medication.

We could not shake our extreme unrest with the idea of including chemo in our arsenal. Discouragement and uncertainty held us back from any decisions.

On Christmas Eve, the day after my diagnosis, my heart was limping. Luke came down and asked me what I was doing. I told him I was journaling, reading the Bible, and asking God to restore my joy. He asked if he could write a message in my journal. He drew a picture of the cross with Jesus on it and said, "Remember that Jesus died for your sins." Then he drew a picture of a cloud next to it and said, "God is above you and watches over you." Then he drew a picture of a person with a sad face with an arrow going up by his head and said, "Don't let Satan control your thoughts." Luke told me he wanted to be a pastor when he grew up. Here he was preaching his first sermon at age five. It lifted my heart and restored right thinking. God can do anything and use anyone, even a young child. (blog post, January 1, 2014)

That sweet moment with Luke just twenty-four hours after my diagnosis ignited a desire in my heart to listen to one voice: Jesus Christ's. The Lord taught me early on in our cancer journey that when the familiar suffocation crept its way inside, I needed to retreat from all cancer info and helpful advice coming from loved ones. Peace came when I was seeking my Healer rather than focusing on my healing. I needed to remind myself that my real quest for the cure had been fulfilled when I had given my heart to Jesus and been given the gift of eternal life.

Jesus Is in Control

Treatment decisions given in an oncology office resemble riding as a front-seat passenger when the light turns green and the driver floors it to maximum acceleration. Pressed backward, you are flattened into the seat as the world blurs by you. This part of our journey was confusing. It was overwhelming. And it was lonely.

During my appointments I noticed my status as a statistic, not an individual. I was reminded at every appointment that this cancer was "treatable but not curable." Not exactly a boost to an already struggling heart.

One day Steve said to me, "Lisa, we all are dying! And God decides when." Relief ran through me! I wasn't alone! The doctors did not know my God, or they would have refrained from slapping on a death-date estimate.

Walking alongside countless others making medical decisions for their own cancer journeys has enabled me to glimpse numerous outcomes.

It remains a mystery to me why some are cured this side of heaven and others are not, even when two people choose the same path of treatment. Only the sovereignty of God quiets the confusing questions surrounding the matter of healing. Henry Frost declares, "The sovereignty of God is not a doctrine which appeals to the natural man. Indeed it is a repellent to him because it creates a situation which is beyond his understanding and control."[1] God and God alone would decide when and where my cancer was cured! I had been set free in Christ to walk in joyful obedience the path He had chosen for me.

I pray that everyone walking through cancer storms will experience the desire for surpassing peace in the midst of their own journeys. This peace comes when we first seek God's kingdom and surrender all to our Medical Director. This peace has come to me not from knowing whether I will be cured from cancer this side of heaven but from immersing myself in Jesus and His written Word. For "great peace have those who love [God's] law" (Ps. 119:165, NIV).

Healthcare

At the time of my diagnosis, I was privileged to already have a supportive and compassionate team of local healthcare professionals, which included my naturopathic primary-care physician, chiropractor, and massage therapist.

God brought my primary-care physician into my life when Ellie was just a toddler. Luke and Ellie had both been hit with insanely high fevers. I hadn't even known that thermometers went that high. She guided us through that difficult week with steadfast calmness and compassion. She has continued to be there for me and our family for seven years now with exceptional grace and kindness.

I first met my gifted chiropractor after Gracie's birth. Her capacity to see the inner me connected her and me at the heart level. She walked me through my recovery after Gracie's difficult birth, a marathon I ran (my third), one more pregnancy and birth (Sammy J's), and the first two years of my cancer diagnosis. (When she told me in the summer of 2015 that she was moving back to the Midwest to start her own practice, I was overjoyed for her but incredibly sad for me. The impact she has had on who I am remains today.)

Another blessing from God came through a gift certificate for a massage I received while pregnant with Ellie. At the age of thirty, I entered a delightful spa in Portland to receive my first-ever massage. Only God could have orchestrated that my first massage would be with such a skilled, intuitive, and compassionate soul. She remains an important part of my life today and is a gift I count over and over again.

These three healthcare professionals consistently came alongside me, ready to help in any way they could as I researched my options for cancer treatment.

Beginning Our Treatment Journey

After much prayer, Steve and I decided to put chemo on the back burner. Instead we began to learn all we could about alternative paths through an essential-oil book, natural-health websites, and some friends. We began juicing, using frankincense essential oil, and making dietary changes. Steve would walk by my green veggie smoothies and say, "Wow, you must love us a lot!" Admittedly, those early smoothies were so terrifying that I plugged my nose while drinking them down. Somewhere along the way, I made the decision not to eat or drink anything I didn't grow to love.

Sadly, the pain from the cancerous lymph nodes that filled my abdomen increased. With follicular non-Hodgkin's lymphoma, sick blood cells can travel to various parts of the body, including the lymph nodes, and form tumors.[2] I later learned that cancer-cell death can cause inflammation as well, but at that time we were convinced the nodes were growing.

So in the middle of January 2014, we packed our young family and made the trip from Portland, Oregon, where we lived, to an integrative cancer-treatment center in Irvine, California. We had chosen this one because it was close to where my sister Lynnette lived. Integrative treatment centers focus on various types of physical treatment as well as emotional and spiritual factors related to cancer. We were able to pay for the trip with partial insurance coverage, financial help from family and friends, a tax return, and our first home-equity loan. God brought in everything we needed to pay for three intensive weeks of high-dose vitamin C therapy, hyperbaric oxygen therapy, and learning about detoxification.

I have now completed the first day of treatment. Whew! Anything new can be challenging. In time, it will get easier handling the details that come when you are in treatments all day with four little ones and a working husband. We are so thankful for Steve being able to work remotely. I absolutely would not be making it without my sisters, Laurie and Lynnette, and my friend Dory right now. It takes an army indeed!

It has been a difficult week. Last night the full impact settled on me that this is where God has led us and that it will not be easy. I best take it one day at a time and not think past that.

It helped so much to know that my sisters had the older three children today and that they were in good hands and having fun. I am praying a huge blessing on my sisters for their hard work. It's not easy taking care of kids all day. I feel very loved right now by them both for putting in such a long day. The people at the treatment center today kept asking, "How in the world are you managing all this with four little kids?" I said, "By God's grace, one hour at a time."

I love meeting the people who are there and learning about their cancer journeys. I had an especially encouraging conversation with a patient who has the same type of cancer as me! She is doing very well and had some good information for me on things that she has been doing. When you have something in common with someone, a bond usually forms. Cancer is the same way. (blog post, January 16, 2014)

Lessons Along the Way

In Irvine Jesus trained the eyes of my soul to scan the landscape of my life for rainbows. In the Northwest, where we lived, it frequently rained at the same time that the sun was shining, resulting in vibrant rainbows. Cancer was now the storm, and Jesus was the sunlight. Rainbows were the result of the light of Jesus shining in the midst of our storm.

A month before my cancer diagnosis, I had read Ann Voskamp's *One Thousand Gifts*. Little did I know that God was preparing my eyes to see rainbows right before I would need this discipline the most. I had completed one month of counting gifts when we found out about the cancer. I made a red-headed foot stomp at the moment of diagnosis and declared with a spit in the enemy's face that I would never, ever, *ever* stop counting blessings. "Make thankfulness your sacrifice to God, and keep the vows you made to the Most High" (Ps. 50:14, NLT). It has now been nearly five years since I entered the fight to "be thankful in all circumstances" (1 Thess. 5:18, NLT). A gift-counting book I started early on is now approaching five thousand gifts, and each gift rises in fragrant praise to the One who is the giver of all good things.

Waiting until a storm has passed to count blessings robs us of the joy Jesus wants us to have in Him. He is higher, better, and more valuable than anything in our sight, including our very lives. My family has experienced an increase in blessings in the most intense moments with cancer. Writing down our rainbow stories enables us to make a return trip to those bright moments when we are in need of encouragement.

I know I should be asleep, but I can't help it tonight! I am staying up to make sure Steve takes his next dose of medication to help him with the intense flu he has. Every day that I am going to the treatment center is like opening a gift. I anticipate what it might be like, who I will meet, what I will learn. This week was full of blessings of all kinds! I met a new friend whom I just love, a sister in Christ. I met two women with breast cancer who shared their stories. I had lots of interesting and good talks with the treatment center staff. It's fun getting to know them. A huge percentage of these wonderful people love their jobs. Many of them will tell you that, but you can also see it just from how they interact with you.

My favorite experience this week was the chance to meet a beautiful and sweet sixteen-year-old girl who is fighting bone cancer. When I saw her walk in with her dad last week, I had a distinct feeling that they loved Jesus! As it turns out, they are Christians, and they go to a small church not far from here. They invited our family to visit and offered babysitting if we ever need it. I cannot wait to hang out with her outside of the time at the treatment center as soon as we can work it out. She is an athlete, and she made the national volleyball team for her age group for the Olympics! Then she found out last summer she had bone cancer.

I love hanging out with high-school and college-age girls, so this is a real treat for me to have met her. It put a huge smile on my face the rest of the day.

Today I had the blessing of a park playdate with my dear friend Dory, who I met when I was eleven years old. She has been taking care of Sammy J a couple days a week. He adores her! People at her son's school asked her whose baby that was, and she told them my story. Guess what?

These families from her son's school, people who don't even know me, just sent home the most delicious food for our family's dinners this weekend! They offered to cook for us. Isn't God good? (blog post, January 24, 2014)

The opportunity we had in Irvine to attack the cancer cells in a way that was not harsh was a gift. The treatments allowed for my immune system to be built up instead of destroyed.

The time we spent in Irvine also provided numerous trials that served to strengthen us for the years ahead. We laughed, cried, and had moments of wondering if all the effort was worth it. Were we doing the right thing as parents to uproot our kids from their routines and take them a thousand miles from home? With each wave of doubt that came, the whispers of Jesus followed with a scripture that has been what I like to call, since cancer began, a "frequent flyer": "Trust Me. 'This is the way, walk in it'" (Isa. 30:21).

I learned to be careful of evaluating decisions based on whether things ended up being smooth or bumpy. It always came back to peace. I saw Jesus provide peace in the most difficult situations. Hard didn't mean we had veered off the path Jesus had for us. God never wastes a bump in the road. Celebrating Luke's sixth birthday in California was a perfect example of that:

Luke and Ellie have been battling high fevers today hitting up over 105. We had attempted, since it is Luke's birthday, to take him to see the ocean, but he didn't last long. Sure enough, when we got him back to the hotel and checked his temperature, it was almost 105. Then a short time later Ellie's spiked over 105.

I was approaching a mommy meltdown. After settling the kids, I left to go to the quiet of the hotel lobby with my journal, headphones, and Bible. God is so very, very good. I begged Him for what I needed to keep

43

a positive perspective on the day. For me, the kids' birthdays have always been super special. So it was hard to have the one child who has been looking forward to Sea World and his birthday party for literally months have it all get cancelled and be lying shivering from ice treatments to bring his fever down.

In my time of reading I realized my thinking was all wrong. I was seeing this day, Luke's sixth birthday, as being about Luke, when it is really about God, who in His intricate plan chose January 26 as the day to bring into this world one amazing boy. Luke's name means "bringer of light," and he has been that for me time and time again in his six years. Today is about celebrating the Lord and the gift that He gave to us in Luke as our precious firstborn son for six years. Today's gift to our family is the reminder that the best gift anyone can ever receive is the one and only gift that can never be taken away—the Pearl of Great Price, Jesus, and eternity with Him. Matthew 13:45-46 shares about Jesus telling His disciples how "the kingdom of heaven is like a merchant looking for fine pearls. When he found one of great value, he went away and *sold everything he had* and bought it!"

I have seen faith in action in a huge way in the last few weeks that I never would have had the blessing of seeing if follicular non-Hodgkin's lymphoma had not become part of our lives. People ask, "How are you doing this?" My honest answer is, "I'm not!" I have so many times when I start to wonder how we will get by just one more hour, especially right now with sick children and high fevers and being unsure if I will even be able to go to treatment! The *only* thing that works for me is looking up to heaven and begging God for help for that moment in whatever way He chooses to send. I can tell you that

He has been, is, and will continue to be faithful in that. (blog post, January 26, 2014)

Trusting in the Dark

We were thrilled when the time came to be back home in Portland. Our tired little family melted right into our cozy beds.

We were learning that treating cancer with natural treatments provided lots of opportunity for trusting with less information than conventional methods offered. An oncologist would have presented us with a plan sounding something like this: "Six cycles of chemo, CT scan part way through, CT scan when done, and you are back to your life if all goes well." Some days it sounded as if it would be a lot easier to try that route and hope it would work. But the fact that the type of lymphoma I had was not likely to go into long-term remission with chemo was a reality we returned to in our harder moments.

I'm not good at it—trusting God in the dark. It's hard not knowing which way the road is going to turn and how fast it will go up and down. It's not unlike the time when I was a teenager going on the roller coaster Space Mountain at Disneyland over and over again. I went on it thirteen times in a row and then it broke down while I was on it. I was shocked to see what it was like when the lights were on! Truly, I'm not sure I would want to ride it with the lights on, the tracks are so close to things and it looks like your head barely would clear them! But what I knew was that I was on the tracks and even if I couldn't see them, they were there.

That is how it is right now. We may not see the road where God is taking us, but it's there, paved exactly the way He wants us to go. If we don't know the way yet, we aren't supposed to know. I was also encouraged tonight by the reminder that trusting in God should not be something we have to do on our own but with the body of believers.

We are thankful to be home. We praise God for always being with us even when we can't always "feel" it. We know He is there. Today, Steve and I took thick blankets and tea and went out on the deck swing to talk and pray. We aren't sure what tomorrow will bring, but we are thankful for the time we had tonight. We pray we will focus on the gifts of each day. (blog post, February 1, 2014)

Seeking the cure is a normal desire. The first waves of my cancer storm had us pleading to Jesus to show us the way to the cure for this type of cancer. In our search for a cure, what we heard was to align our search with God's Word, seek first God's kingdom, follow the Lord wherever He called us, and give our best efforts but trust Him with the outcome (see Ps. 4:5).

Dear Jesus, You inhabit eternity. Yet You also inhabit me. Oh, the wonder of it all! Make me aware of Your very presence inside my body today. You command every process inside me. You hold the number of my days in Your hand. Send Your peace through me right now. Let it reach the very tips of my fingers and toes and into every cell. Let it release muscles tight with wearisome thoughts that are not from You. I let go. I lean back into Your strong arms. Amen.

Cancer Is Not My Fight

I have had many dear friends die from cancer overtaking their bodies. But I have never known a cancer patient who has "lost his fight" against cancer. We can't lose a battle that was never ours to fight.

Each time one of my children falls and scrapes him or herself, I am reminded that our Creator designed our bodies to heal themselves. Usually all my kids need is a Band-Aid and a kiss from Momma. When five-year-old Luke crashed on his bike, God healed him through the hands of a trained physician who stitched his chin up beautifully.

God can and does use man to treat and heal. But the absolute source of all healing is our almighty God.

Cancer is not mine to "beat." I give my Spirit-led best efforts, but it is Jesus who directs my immune system. It is Jesus alone who heals. He is *God*. He decides when healing will come. "A person cannot receive even one thing unless it is given him from heaven" (John 3:27). Because Jesus died and rose again, and because I have placed my complete trust in Him as my Savior, I am guaranteed eternity with Him in a perfect body. He initiated my healing on the cross, and the transaction is guaranteed to be complete when I am home in heaven with Him. While Jesus may heal my body from cancer here on Earth, unless He returns first, I will experience an earthly death. Scripture tells us that death is the final enemy to be destroyed (see 1 Cor. 15:26). And destroyed it will be!

I have met numerous people who have been victorious cancer patients. They are with Jesus now. They have won in every way. The true battle they were fighting was not against cancer but for perspective and perseverance. Victory came when they chose hope, joy, love, and thankfulness in the midst of cancer. Victory came when they sought to live a purposeful life centered on loving God and loving others.

We are in a fight to persevere. Doubt, discouragement, fear, despair—all will visit us in the valleys of life. But God has given us His Word as a sword and our faith as a shield. With them we can be protected from the enemy's arrows. The key to the fight for perspective is to fasten our eyes on the cross.

The God-Confident Life

How we feel when facing cancer is not unlike what King Asa must have felt when he saw an Ethiopian army of a million soldiers and three hundred chariots on their way to attack him. He knew his army was no match for his opponents. Asa cried out to the Lord, "'There is none like you to help, between the mighty and the weak. Help us, O LORD our God, for we rely on you, and in

your name we have come against this multitude.' . . . So the
LORD defeated the Ethiopians before Asa and before Judah, and
the Ethiopians fled" (2 Chron. 14:11–12). Asa turned his God-
confident eyes to the battlefield and watched the Lord defeat
the Ethiopians.

Confidence attracts. We flock to doctors who confidently
present treatment plans that have high success rates. Yet as all
too many of us have experienced, these treatment plans can
fail. At times even the most highly trained physician lacks answers. Confidence in self is no better—it steals the peace that
God promises when we set our minds on His Spirit (see Rom.
8:6). Only confidence in God will truly bring us answers.

Asa's son Jehoshaphat took the throne of Judah after his
father. He was thirty-five years old when he began to reign.
The life of Jehoshaphat is recorded in 2 Chronicles 17–20 and
holds a goldmine of treasure for the cancer patient. Jehoshaphat
knew what fear was and where to go when fear came knocking.

Second Chronicles 20 gives insight into what the king experienced emotionally as a vast army from Edom was approaching. Jehoshaphat was afraid! He proclaimed a fast and sought
to seek the Lord (see 2 Chron. 20:3). Israel declared their lack of
strength to face this battle: "We have no power to face this vast
army that is attacking us. We do not know what to do, but our
eyes are on you" (2 Chron. 20:12, NIV). Jehoshaphat took his
eyes off the storm and put them on the Savior. Then the Spirit
of the Lord came on Jahaziel, and he gave a message from God
to the people: "Do not be afraid or discouraged because of this
vast army. For the battle is *not* yours, but God's. . . . You will not
have to fight this battle. . . . Do not be discouraged. Go out to
face them tomorrow, and the LORD will be with you" (2 Chron.
20:15–17, NIV).

Jehoshaphat's story gives us action steps we should take
when trouble comes:

- Set our faces to seek God (see 2 Chron. 20:3).
- Proclaim a fast (see 2 Chron. 20:3).
- Seek help from God (see 2 Chron. 20:4).
- Acknowledge God's power and might over all things (see 2 Chron. 20:6).
- Recount past miracles and provision from God (see 2 Chron. 20:7–8).
- Admit our powerlessness (see 2 Chron. 20:12).
- God is with us, so we should refuse fear, stand firm, and watch God work (see 2 Chron. 20:15–17).
- Pray with our faces to the ground (see 2 Chron. 20:18).
- Praise God before He works; praise Him as He works; praise Him after He works (see 2 Chron. 20:19, 22, 27).

A Balm for Discouragement

When we are tempted to be discouraged, God often gives us glimpses of His love that help us lift our eyes back to Him. He used my son Luke to minister to me soon after we returned home from Irvine:

One of my favorite moments from this week came last night with Luke. We cuddle at nighttimes quite often for a few minutes before he goes to bed. Last night he had a story to tell me. He told me about a little boy who had the best momma in the world. This little boy loved his momma more than she could ever imagine. No matter how old he got, he would marry this momma when he was old enough. Then he said, "Momma, that momma is you!" Of course my heart melted, and I immediately told the Lord, "Thank You so much for that." It came after a discouraging couple of days and reminded me how uniquely special all children are—each with his or her own strengths, challenges, and joy buttons! Luke's joy button lies in his emotional and spiritual sensitivity.

Last night we invited him to join in on our starry night of prayer. He climbed up in my lap and cuddled up with the blanket and began asking all sorts of questions. My favorite lighthearted one was, "Momma, how big do you think God's big toe is?" It reminded me of the personhood of God, how He became man and the gift that He gave us in coming in the form of man to die on the cross to give us a way to restore right relationship with Him. Sometimes we lose that connection with God as our Father.

It would be very easy for me right now to go down the road of being the "imperfect parent," as I have no way of managing all four of my kids right now. Good! It's the best place to be in, because I never should have been thinking I could do it to begin with. God is the only perfect parent out there. The rest of us will falter on a moment-by-moment basis, and the best thing we can do is point our kids to Christ as the perfect parent—able to be both Father and Mother to them at all times. Just imagine climbing on God's lap, knowing He can meet your every need. Beautiful imagery, and yet it's real! (blog post, February 9, 2014)

Another encouragement came when I flew down to Irvine for treatment a couple more times. One of my favorite doctors at the Irvine treatment center was in charge of electromagnetic treatments. On one of my trips, he shared with me a story about a girl with leukemia who had been healed after receiving laser treatments from a German chiropractor in Sacramento.

I would be flying through Sacramento on my way home, and I felt a strong pull to visit with this chiropractor. This is a moment I look back on and think, *Wow, I really did that?* Yes. I rented a car for three hours during a layover just to see this man. God has His purpose in all things. It was through this layover and my appointment with this eighty-year-old chiropractor trained in Germany that I was led to a specialized treatment that would help adjust the terrain inside my body where the cancer cells were multiplying.

I walked into this chiropractor's office and saw this man barely alive shuffling around. What in the world was I doing there? At certain moments I have inwardly giggled at myself with Jesus, thanking Him for His vast grace in this journey. This was one of those moments, and I share a smile with Jesus now as I remember it.

While waiting to be called back to the treatment room, I picked up a thin book this chiropractor had written on natural cancer treatment and found a page titled "Precision Intestinal Oxidative Hydrotoning" (PIOH). The words drew me in immediately. It spoke of cleaning the blood, lightening the load on the lymphatic system, and getting oxygen to every cell in the body. My meeting with the chiropractor was nice, but it was uneventful. I knew beyond any shadow of doubt that discovering PIOH was why God had brought me to that little office.

After returning home and talking with Steve, I called the phone number I had found in the book to get help with finding a local PIOH practitioner.

There was only one—in the entire world! I was ecstatic to find out that his office was located in Washington State, but my heart sank when I found out he was currently in Alaska for three months. With the level of pain I was having, I could not wait three months. I looked at Steve. He looked at me. I was going to Alaska!

I spent nine days in Alaska on a beautiful serene island in early March 2014, two and a half months after my official diagnosis. Though I was alone physically, Jesus was my faithful companion.

It was difficult being so far from Steve and the kids, but our sweet Jesus held me tenderly. He took care of my every need, giving me repeated assurances in my heart that I was right where I was meant to be.

I'm halfway through my time here in Alaska. I will say that this last week has been the hardest I've had since November, when we first found out about the cancer. Right now not much makes sense physically, and we don't know what's causing certain problems. We could take our pick of several possibilities. I find my heart longing to dwell on what I know is true and real, and to be held by Jesus and allow Him to guide.

Here is what I know about our God. He is the one and only true God. His love for us is best portrayed through the death of His only Son on the cross—His gift to us that, if we accept it, will give us eternity with Him. God is compassionate and rich in mercy. He is my joy giver. He quietly holds me when I need to process emotions. He is slow to anger and abounding in love. His Spirit lives in me, providing perseverance through this very challenging time. Our God is Healer. He is everywhere at once. There is nowhere we can go where He is not there. He is creative. He paints amazing Alaskan sunsets. He is the God who sees. He is the giver of good gifts. He has given me the most incredible husband, who is a gift I am just singing praise to God for this week. He has given me four precious children. He has given us a wonderful support system and people praying all over the world. He takes my doubts and gives grace. He has provided people to call me on the phone to pray during times of extra attacks on my mind. He provides laughter. He is who He says He is. He comforts in His nearness. He is enough.

He is our safe haven. He shuts the mouths of lions. He is a consuming fire.

It says in the book of Matthew that the greatest commandment is to love the Lord our God with all our hearts, minds, and souls. That means surrendering everything else that battles for our attention. I am finding this to be the hardest test I've had yet, as I have constant nerve tingles that are best described as antagonistic. You know what I do now to combat how it makes me feel? I sing. I am not blessed with a great voice, but to God it's a joyful noise. I believe joy follows obedience. We have dark times, but if I do the next right thing, cry when needed, and pray, joy returns. Suffering comes in all different shapes and sizes, but it is a vehicle that allows us to experience a glimpse of what Jesus did. Jesus also wept. He felt emotions. I can't wait to hear Him laugh. Belle [Ellie] asks all the time to hug Jesus. I love that! The best part is that since we have His Holy Spirit in us, we can get that hug as we spend time in quiet connection with the Lord.

I am praising God for the feeling of peace that I'm doing the right thing right now. I praise Him that in His timing He has always directed our steps. (blog post, March 4, 2014)

Through the treatments I received in Alaska, I experienced significantly reduced abdominal swelling and pain, increased energy and circulation, and a renewed bounce to my step. My CT scan in early March resulted in the good news that one of the two big nodes that had been causing me pain had shrunk. I returned to Alaska two more times that March. I made many beautiful memories, including one of Steve and me traveling there together for our eleventh wedding anniversary.

My PIOH practitioner has since come alongside me numerous times in challenging situations with individualized attention and kindness. Even after forty years in his line of work, he remains a student of his field, resulting in tweaks and tricks that help each person who walks through his doors to leave healthier than when he or she arrived.

What a kindness it is when Jesus sends us personalized blessings to encourage us in our storms.

Second Opinions

A month later, however, my pain level increased significantly. Doubts crept in. We began questioning if the cancer really was the slow-growing form of lymphoma. The doctors were "fairly certain," but they had left a window open for error. Good friends of ours had recommended MD Anderson Cancer Center in Houston, Texas, as the place to go for top lymphoma specialists in the country. We prayerfully decided to go for a second opinion.

I spent five days at MD Anderson on the lymphoma floor. Imagine that—an entire hospital floor dedicated to lymphoma patients! We had the best care from nurses and doctors. We were visited by dear friends of ours who lived in Houston, and we even met new friends on the lymphoma floor. We were discharged in time to attend the Easter service at our friends' church before we flew home.

Our time at MD Anderson gave us a confirmed diagnosis and scans showing slight improvements over the original scans. The oncologist there was, surprisingly, not a fan of chemotherapy for this type of cancer, because, as she said, "it always grows back." We left with affirmation from the Lord that we should stay on the natural path we were on, keep breastfeeding Sammy J, and trust Him to show us the next steps.

Fight for Perseverance by Resting in Jesus

We love watching "honkers" fly overhead as they head south for the winter. The lead goose has a tough job. In my fight for perseverance, daily I ask myself if I am trying to take the lead. I so often do! Jesus wants to tuck me in behind Him and be my hiding place.

In the book of Job, God brings up His faithful servant to Satan not once but twice. Job gets past round one with his faith intact. Then he faces round two. We may be hit with trial after trial. James 5:11 says that those who persevere are considered blessed, and it uses Job as an example. Paul tells us that when we persevere through hard times, it produces character in us. That character will produce a hope that cannot ever disappoint (see Rom. 5:3-5).

But if in your effort to persevere you are like me and find yourself flying out front today in the flying V-formation, Jesus longs to tuck you behind Him and take the lead. The air is calmer when Jesus flies first. With Jesus in the lead, the fight for perseverance becomes as simple as keeping our eyes on Him. When our eyes are on Jesus, our souls can see two things: the cross of Jesus and the finish line at eternity's shore, where Jesus is waiting to welcome us home.

Clouds of weariness and discouragement vanish when we consider what Jesus went through on the cross. Jesus set the example for us by keeping heaven's joy in view as He suffered for our sins on the cross (see Heb. 12:1-3). His death didn't guarantee us lives free from suffering but His presence with us while we go through difficult times. My race is different from yours, but we can love and encourage one another along the way, knowing we will all be with Jesus at the finish-line celebration.

The immune system is an intricate and beautiful gift from our Creator, designed to help our bodies heal themselves. Although

I believe in giving my best efforts, I do not believe that I am ultimately responsible for my own healing. Self-healing is a weight I was not created to bear up under. Coming to Jesus, putting our open hands before Him, giving Him our whole hearts, and trusting Him with every cell of our bodies is how we receive the true victory. Jesus tells us, "Come to me, all who labor and are heavy laden, and I will give you rest. Take my yoke upon you, and learn from me, for I am gentle and lowly in heart, and you will find rest for your souls. For my yoke is easy, and my burden is light" (Matt. 11:28–30). Rest is something we all long for—true rest. Jesus offers true rest that is so sweet to our souls.

Oh, how God delights in the self-emptied vessel. He is ready to swoop in and fill every self-emptied crevice of our hearts. King Asa lacked confidence in going to war against such a large army. He cried out to God for help, placing his trust in God. When facing the impossible, King Asa received the confidence that comes when the source is God and not self. We can do the same.

Whether our physical healing, which was initiated when Jesus died and rose again, is completed here on Earth or there in heaven, we can choose to live God-confident lives, knowing He is fighting for us. We can choose to zero in on the Savior, not the waves.

> Yours, O LORD, is the greatness and the power and the glory and the victory and the majesty, for all that is in the heavens and in the earth is yours. Yours is the kingdom, O LORD, and you are exalted as head above all. Both riches and honor come from you, and you rule over all. In your hand are power and might, and in your hand it is to make great and to give strength to all. And now we thank you, our God, and praise your glorious name. (1 Chron. 29:11–13)

Man's Wisdom

No two cancers are identical. Hodgkin's lymphoma is highly responsive to chemotherapy. Non-Hodgkin's lymphoma is diverse, including both aggressive and slow-growing types. And that's just the world of lymphoma! I can only imagine the complexities many cancer patients face with their own individual diagnoses.

Not only does cancer behave differently depending on its type, but each patient is a unique creation of our almighty God. This means that two patients with the exact same type of cancer can have the same treatment but completely different responses. Ask Jesus. Always, always ask Jesus!

As my level of nausea and pain both grew and shrank in June 2014, Steve and I decided to spend a week in Washington so I could receive further treatment from my PIOH practitioner, who was now back from Alaska, as well as get local vitamin C IVs with a naturopathic doctor who worked in the same area.

The father of one of the families I had babysat for in high school was a lead pastor of a church near the treatment centers. Steve and I had visited the church a few times when we had traveled through that area. We prayerfully contacted him to ask if anyone in the church could help us with our children and a place to stay when we traveled up for treatment. Sometimes when we are in the thick of hard, love from Jesus swoops in through His body, the church. Oh, such love the Father has for His children! The response to our request was overwhelming. Not only were we provided a place to stay, but the young families Sunday school class adopted our children for playdates while Steve worked and I had treatments!

Fork in the Road

Nausea is a beast. When I was a kid, I did anything to avoid vomiting. On one family camping trip, my little sister turned her sweet face toward me in the night just in time to vomit in my face. Let's just say I didn't like tangerines for a long time after that. That experience furthered my resolve as a child to avoid vomiting at all costs. But after ten months of staying on the natural treatment path, my growing lymph nodes were pressing on my liver and gallbladder. Nausea became my constant companion.

The middle of August found us staring down a fork in the road—should we continue our natural path or turn to conventional cancer treatment?

My Lisa plan had crept in and taken over more of my heart with each passing month. God had used the doctor's report that my kind of cancer was "incurable" to encourage us to look further in His medicine cabinet, and with all we had learned, my plan had closed the door to anything but natural medicine.

My plan extended into the future too: I would continue breast-feeding Sammy until he was two, my kids would grow up, and we would pay off our college loans; then Steve and I would travel the world looking for nontoxic cancer treatments. *Retirement would be a much better time for cancer, Lord—right? Or how about at least after my kids are out of diapers?*

I worked hard to kick the cancer cells out. I read cancer book after cancer book. I tried everything from the Budwig diet to Essiac tea, essential oils, detoxification, and juicing all things green. I had an overflowing cupboard filled with bottle after bottle of "you gotta try this" supplements.

Yet the lymph nodes grew.

We considered two options ahead of us: a cancer hospital in Mexico that we had learned about or the first line of treatment from conventional medicine. *Which way, Lord, which way?*

This is what the LORD says—your Redeemer, the Holy One of Israel: "I am the LORD your God, who teaches you what is good for you and leads you along the paths you should follow." (Isa. 48:17, NLT)

These whispers of Jesus through our reading of Scripture and prayer continuously provided an escape from the tentacles of doubt and fear that threatened our peace. God's Word is 100 percent true. It is our source of wisdom and the guide to all decisions that we make in this life, even medical ones. Especially medical ones. God promises that His Word will be a lamp to our feet and a light to our paths (see Ps. 119:105). God's Word should be the first place we go for wisdom, before the medical office. It is through spending time with Jesus that we know which medical office to go to and what to do with the information we receive while we are there.

"Wisdom . . . cannot be bought with gold. It cannot be purchased from silver. . . . God alone understands the way to wisdom;

he knows where it can be found, for he looks throughout the whole earth and sees everything under the heavens. He decides how hard the winds should blow and how much rain should fall. . . . And this is what He says to all humanity: 'The fear of the Lord is true wisdom; to forsake evil is real understanding'" (Job 28:12-28, NLT). Taking time to wait may feel scary when we receive a cancer diagnosis, but it's worth finding a quiet place, even going away for a few days, to ask Jesus what to do. When we are Spirit-led to a treatment choice, faith will move us forward with joy and peace.

God Hears

Pain is antagonistic. Nausea is debilitating. Neither is helpful for having a clear mind to make decisions. During that hard month of August 2014, I sat in our sauna one day and pleaded with God to speak to me. Frustration welled up inside me at the lack of an easy path, a clear step-by-step plan of how I was going to become cancer free! I needed to know that God had a path for me. As I sat listening to the radio, God provided a reminder that He hears my prayer! Here's what I wrote about that day:

I was sitting in the sauna listening to the radio earlier today and caught a glimpse of Luke playing and dancing to the music in the corner of the garage. He brings such joy to my momma heart. His name means "bringer of light." When Gracie was just a few months old, this little boy prayed for God to put a baby boy in my tummy. He had two sisters but no brother. God said yes, and Samuel Jeremiah was born less than a year later. Samuel means "God heard." We were led to that name because of a four-year-old's faith-filled prayers.

Little did I know that God would use the story of these two brothers, my beloved sons, to remind me today that He is the God of the impossible. He brings His light to every situation and hears every prayer on our hearts! Just as I finished this Spirit-guided journey of thankfulness in looking back at God's faithfulness, the Fish Family Name Game came on the radio![1] I have never really thought about calling in, as many times as I have heard it. Today though—drum roll—the name was Samuel! I felt the familiar quickening of my heartbeat when God asks me to do something. I called in and burst into tears as I shared our story of this little baby boy named Samuel Jeremiah Engelman. The tears were more a result of the realization that, once again, God hears. (blog post, August 14, 2014)

The Lord reminded us that summer day that He was laying railroad tracks ahead for us. The path He was taking us on was unique and purposeful. He is faithful, His love unchanging. My name, Lisa, means "consecrated to God," set apart for His service. There is nothing good in me apart from Jesus. His love overwhelms me. My role is to be willing and surrendered to the tracks ahead, trusting that God will close and open doors according to His kingdom purposes.

In the heat of the sauna that day, the Lord whispered to my heart, "My child, My child, look at the tracks behind you! I have carried you over so many mountains, and others I have allowed you to pass by at the very last minute! Look at your sweet sons. Let them remind you that I am the bringer of light and that I hear every prayer before it even leaves your lips. Be strong and courageous, for I am with you wherever you go. I am God; there is none like me. My purposes will stand! I make known the end from the beginning, things present from things to come. Be still, Steve and Lisa, and know that I am *God*!"

Not an Easy Road

The Lord promises to lead us "in paths of righteousness for his name's sake" (Ps. 23:3). We held that promise close as we chose to go to the cancer hospital in Mexico.

Our bodies are the temple in which the living God resides. We are not our own, and we are to glorify God in our bodies (see 1 Cor. 6:19–20). My heart's desire was to protect my healthy cells while cancer was being treated—something chemo would not do—and I couldn't deny that desire. I was grateful that God had provided a path for us to intensively treat cancer with non-toxic treatments.

The Lord worked in miraculous ways to provide care at home for our precious littles from my sister Laurie and my momma. While my heart ached that my arms would not be able to hold my babies while Steve and I were gone, I had peace in knowing that we were being obedient to what God was asking of us.

I learned on my first trip to Mexico not to assume that following God's path is synonymous with an easy road. From our inability to speak Spanish to my needing a PET scan to my growing pain from treatments that were working but causing swelling, we experienced plenty of bumps.

Confusion crept in when we realized that we couldn't afford to pay for the number of weeks of treatment I would need. We had spent almost a year using natural medicine. We had received financial gifts, but we had also taken out a home loan that was dwindling. We ended up staying only one week.

Local Treatment Begins

God used that shorter-than-expected trip to Mexico to prepare my heart and body for what Steve and I finally decided would come next: my first round of Western medicine. The doctors at the clinic in Mexico agreed that my body was now "more prepared" for Western medicine's harsh treatments. I wasn't quite so sure and found myself still hoping for a way out.

I cannot lie. Deciding to use Western medicine was an excruciatingly difficult decision. We placed our trust in Jesus that we were doing the best we could with our given circumstances. We were relying on God to carry us through, to be our Teacher in the midst of the hardships that accompany Western medicine cancer treatments.

I started immunochemotherapy in September 2014. I went to the local oncology clinic every four weeks for two consecutive days until my last treatment in early February 2015. I received one immunotherapy drug and one chemotherapy drug. The treatments I had were not as harsh as some. The side effects externally were absent. We continued to travel up to Washington for PIOH during this time.

Because I believe in God's control over all things, I knew He had a purpose for the months at the oncology clinic. The treatments I went through at that local clinic gifted us sweet companionship with beautiful people we met over the years because of shared experiences.

I will always be grateful to God for the laughter and lighthearted moments that lit up those tough months. As I mentally prepared for my second chemo treatment in October 2014, I was in a silly mood. I had been thinking about Christmas gifts for the children and not only wrote a song but sang it loudly in my closet. A strange choice for a chemo pump-up song, but it brought me much-needed giggles:

'Twas the night before chemo
When, all through the house,
Not an Engelbabe was stirring,
Not even a mouse.
The prep for each child's tomorrow all done with care,
This song has gone on as long as I dare.

One benefit of conventional treatment is that it became easier for me during those months to answer people's questions concerning how I was doing. For the first time in my cancer journey, I had tangible answers to give—things like, "I'm done with four treatments so far." For six months I had a plan in place. On the downside, I wasn't as desperate to ask God about my steps for the morrow, because the next step was planned for me by the oncologist.

I will be honest. On one hand, it was a break from the turmoil of navigating the path less traveled. On the other hand, the deepest parts of me knew I was just doing my best to choose to be positive in a situation in which I didn't feel I had a choice. We had no money to do anything at this point but treatments that were covered by insurance—which meant chemo. The doctor met with me every couple weeks, reminding me that there was no cure for this type of cancer but that we were "turning back the clock"—buying me more time to live.

There's Room for Two

The day before my mid-treatment CT scan, I considered what it would be like to be slid into a cold machine. It seemed not unlike the cave that Elijah had hidden in when God had met him.

Elijah was on the run. The evil queen Jezebel was after his life, since the 450 prophets of Baal had been killed at Elijah's command.

Elijah had given his life to helping Israel keep God's covenants. Thoughts of failure depressed him. Elijah was convinced that he was the only prophet left standing who was following God. First Kings 19:4 voices Elijah's discouragement: "Take my life; I am no better than my ancestors" (NIV). Translated, "I'm no better than anyone else who has tried, and look where it's gotten me. I give up!"

Feeling afraid, discouraged, and isolated, Elijah lay down and fell asleep in exhaustion. He slept under a tree, not bothering to hide, since death is what he was hoping for. God met him in his brokenness, tending first to his physical needs through an angel bringing him food and water. And not just any food but warm bread (see 1 Kings 19:6). His tummy warmed with food, Elijah had the strength to journey to a cave at Mount Horeb, where he spent the night.

Now that Elijah's physical needs had been tended to, God cared for Elijah's center for processing emotions—his heart. I love how God approached Elijah in the cave in his time of discouragement. He could have reprimanded Elijah, but God chose a jaw-dropping reminder of His power and control over all nature and then contrasted that with His gentle whisper: "Elijah, go stand on the mountain in My presence, for I'm about to pass by." "Then a great and powerful wind tore the mountains apart and shattered the rocks before the LORD, but the LORD was not in the wind. After the wind there was an earthquake, but the LORD was not in the earthquake. After the earthquake came a fire, but the LORD was not in the fire. And after the fire came a gentle whisper" (1 Kings 19:11-12, NIV).

God is all-powerful and controls everything. He is in the earthquake and in the ripple of a peaceful lake. He is in our joy-filled birthday celebrations and in our silence-filled caves of sorrow. Whatever cave we are facing today, the voice of the Lord meets us in a gentle whisper: "Remember Me? There's room for two. I AM."

My mid-treatment CT scan showed only a partial response to chemo. Not what we were hoping for, but we were not surprised. I had two cycles of immunochemotherapy remaining to take another punch at those sneaky cancer cells. We prayed it would do more than the first treatments under God's mighty hand.

From the Chemo Room

I see a girl younger than me. Another young life changed by cancer. Another soul sick to her stomach, sitting across from me. I want to help her, but I'm connected to the drip myself. Cancer knows no boundaries—it affects young and old alike. Next to me is a beautiful woman with breast cancer adorned in a bright and happy pink scarf. She is surrounded with love. Her people are here to support her. The young girl, she is alone. I wish I could change seats to be beside her. Today cancer crowds this room.

With this indolent type of cancer, the doctors don't like to use the words "remission" or "cure." We hear statements like "This treatment should turn the clock way back" or "We hope the lymphoma stays suppressed for quite a while."

Jesus Christ is absolutely the last word. Revelation 20:10 tells us that the devil will be thrown into the lake of fire and tormented there day and night forever! God will have the last word in the end times and in any circumstance in our lives. While I am grateful for the healthcare professionals the Lord has provided to help me, ultimately it is God Himself who has determined my already-numbered days.

Abraham knew that God would have the last word in his life. God had promised him descendants outnumbering the stars in the sky! Abraham did not allow his circumstances of being quite past childbearing years to define his future but trusted that God would indeed do as He had said. God's power is far greater than any problem we face. (journal entry, January 6, 2015)

When we were nearing the end of the first round of conventional treatment, I looked Steve straight in the eyes and spoke some tough words: "Sweetheart, this doesn't feel right to me. I know it seems right to everyone else. I didn't know what else to do. But sweetie, would you support me if I decided to no longer choose chemo? Even if it means doing nothing at all?"

Steve wrapped me up with an affirming hug, committing with me not to allow fear to make any future decisions. We would be strong and courageous. We would not be afraid or terrified, because the Lord our God went with us; He would never leave us or forsake us (see Deut. 31:6).

Bridge Crossing

During my chemo treatment months, six-year-old Luke landed in the children's ER with abdominal pain. The doctors came in and told him he needed surgery to remove his appendix. I was at home with our other three little ones, not feeling well from chemo, when the phone rang with my sweet six-year-old's fearful voice on the phone. "Momma, I'm afraid of surgery!"

My heart ached not to be there to wrap him up in my arms. I told him to close his eyes and imagine that he was at a big park with an amazing playground. On the far side of the playground was a big, scary-looking bridge. The name of that bridge was "Surgery." But right now Jesus was standing right by him, on the opposite side of the park from the bridge, wanting to play together at the playground.

"Luke, if Jesus wants you to go across that scary-looking bridge, it's because He will carry you across. You will not have to be afraid. If you choose to run over to it now, you would be going by yourself, and it would be very scary!" Luke promised me to stay holding Jesus' hand.

A short time later the staff looked over the imaging again to make sure of the diagnosis before they took Luke into surgery. The radiologist said, "There's been a transcription error. I said the appendix was compressible, not incompressible." That meant Luke had a perfectly healthy appendix! He came home at midnight and came running over to me. "Momma, I stayed with Jesus, and He didn't take me across the scary bridge!" Luke's experience became an event I have frequently looked back to when needing the reminder not to run ahead of the Lord but to clasp His hand with childlike trust.

Proverbs 3:1–8 has become a favorite passage of mine to meditate on and pray through whenever I am faced with a new medical decision or health concern. I want God's wisdom, not my own, for "there is not a greater enemy to the fear of the Lord in the heart, than self-conceit of our own wisdom."[2] Taking deep breaths, coming into awareness of my union with Him, I pray this Scripture passage: "Jesus, I will not forget Your teaching, but let my heart keep Your commandments, for length of days and years of life and peace they will add to me. Let me not forsake steadfast love and faithfulness; bind them around my neck; write them on the tablet of my heart so I will find favor and good success in Your sight and man's. I will trust in You with all my heart and not lean on my own understanding. In all my ways I acknowledge You, and You will make straight my paths. I will not be wise in my own eyes. I fear You, Lord, and I turn away from evil. It will be healing to my flesh and refreshment to my bones."

Do we take the path that is expected or the path to which we are called? The two paths may coincide. They may not. The Lord "gives intuition to the heart and instinct to the mind" (Job 38:36, NLT). It is the spirit in man, the breath of the Almighty, that makes him understand (see Job 32:8). We can search Scripture, come to God in prayer, and trust Him, even if He takes us outside what is normal or expected. We follow Jesus in all areas of life because we trust His care for us. We follow Him because we were created to find full satisfaction in Him and enjoy Him forever. We follow Him because, as I learned on my first trip to Mexico, *Dios es Dios. Siempre.*

God is God. Always.

Anything's Possible

During each of my pregnancies, I searched for a verse I could pray over our baby throughout the days of his or her life. After four years of longing for a child, on May 20, 2007, I had my first positive pregnancy test! Luke Daniel Engelman was on the way! His verse came quickly: "Nothing is impossible with God" (Luke 1:37, NLT). When I looked into little Luke's eyes for the first time, on January 26, 2008, his life verse was already being reflected. "See, Momma? Nothing is impossible with God. Here I am!" The Lord has used my firstborn son numerous times during our cancer journey to be my gentle reminder to me that anything's possible.

After our last scheduled chemo treatment in February 2015, the local oncologist said we wouldn't do another scan, since the type of cancer I had was known to remain even after chemo. He reassured me, however, that the clock had been turned back.

During the chemo months, I had spent time reading more on natural treatments. I had learned about the harm of CT scans due to their use of radiation, and I cringed at the dozen I'd had in one year! I decided that after this I would have no more CT scans but would instead request MRIs, which do not use radiation.

I had a break from any scheduled treatments until starting up local high-dose vitamin C IVs that spring. An ultrasound in June that year showed that the two bigger lymph nodes were still enlarged. The four to eight years that the oncologist thought he had turned back my clock ended up being four months.

We were devastated but not shocked. In my inner depths I had known chemo hadn't worked. I had been hoping I was wrong, but I wasn't surprised by the results.

I was taunted by the word "impossible . . . impossible . . . impossible." My hopes to parent my children through their teenage years, dance at their weddings, hold my grandbabies all became blurry.

Wrong Choices

Have you ever felt that you had made a wrong choice? Or maybe you have put in all you had financially, emotionally, and physically toward a treatment and didn't get the result you wanted. This is how I felt after chemo.

I love the story of King Amaziah of Judah. Amaziah had hired one hundred thousand soldiers from Israel to fight for him, when a man of God came to visit him and declared, "Hey, don't use those guys; the Lord is not with them!" Amaziah responded, "But what about all that money I just put into hiring them?" The man of God says, "The LORD is able to give you much more than this" (2 Chron. 25:9).

Jesus has purpose in every single decision we have ever made. Numerous times in history He has been sovereign over wrong choices. Finding peace in those times of frustration and doubting over our past choices comes from remembering that God is God and we are not. Through the Spirit's strength, we should continue to give our surrendered best efforts, but God is in charge of the outcomes of our decisions. God's sovereign control over our lives releases us from being stuck in the mud of "if onlys."

The Glass Sea Tunnel

What if when we pray for deliverance, God says, "Wait"? What if the escape route He chooses is deliverance through our circumstances, not from them?

As the Israelites were leaving Egypt, they arrived at the Red Sea. They were stuck between two impossible situations: the Egyptians closing in on them from behind and the looming Red Sea preventing their forward progress. The Lord's directive to them is the same one He gives to us when we face an impossible situation. The same God who says that all things are possible with Him gave the Israelites in Exodus 14:13–14 four directives: (1) fear not, (2) stand firm, (3) watch the Lord rescue you, and (4) be still. This being "still" can be thought of as "letting our arms hang." Take a breath, drop those shoulders, and let our arms hang. As we breathe out, we release our control, bitterness, frustration, and unbelief. Tension dissipates with His gentle whispers: "Trust Me, My child; I AM fighting for you."

All night long the Lord drove back the waters into two towering walls, leaving a path on dry land for the Israelites to walk through. Imagine what it must have been like to take those first few steps, then slowly making it to the middle and tentatively glancing up, locking eyes with the towering walls of water on either side.

For the Israelites, their rescue from slavery included hardship. Our rescues will too. We will one day be welcomed into the heavenly kingdom, but the journey there will not be without trials.

"Through many tribulations we must enter the kingdom of God" (Acts 14:22).

Seasons of tribulation, whether short and gut punching or long and antagonistic, will often raise confusing questions. When my soul cries out in my darker hours and answers don't come, sometimes it helps me to sing "Jesus Loves Me" out loud. I declare that Jesus loves me, because the Bible tells me so! At the sound of His name, the power of His presence moves out all confusion as His peace permeates.

In times of adversity, the Lord promises that His guiding voice will be with us, gently whispering to us, "This is the way, walk in it" (Isa. 30:21). His provision may not be a path around our sea of hard, but He will equip us for our voyage through it.

Standing in the middle of our own Red Sea crossing, we tentatively reach out toward the water, and our hands meet glass. We are safely encapsulated in the glass sea tunnel. Though the walls of sea water tower on each side, we know we are safe in God's purposeful cocoon. We see precious Jesus a few steps ahead of us, His light shining just enough on the path ahead for us to see His outstretched hand. His words come: "Take courage! It is I. Don't be afraid" (Matt. 14:27, NIV).

Luke's Lemonade for Momma

Cancer brings opportunities for us to lean hard into God. My stubborn swollen lymph nodes were used by God to gift our family a miracle in August 2015.

Steve and I prayerfully decided not to continue down the path of current Western medicine treatments, which would continue to weaken my limping immune system. But we were stopped from a full dive into intensive natural cancer treatments by the cost. Most Western medicine healthcare is more expensive than alternative medicine. The difference is that insurance tends to cover the majority of Western medicine but offers next to nothing for alternative.

The total bill for my six monthly immunochemotherapy treatments surpassed one hundred sixty-five thousand dollars. My insurance, however, paid for all but a thirty-dollar co-pay for each of the nine treatment days and six follow-up visits. I did not understand why my insurance company would pay for chemo but not for natural treatments, especially for a cancer that doctors consider incurable.

I had discovered another alternative cancer-treatment center in Mexico called Hope4Cancer; it was less than a mile away from the one we had gone to the year before but hadn't been able to afford to stay at. We had tucked Hope4Cancer away for a time when I would need intensive cancer treatment again. We felt sure it was the right place for us, but having finished chemo fairly recently, we did not expect to go for a while.

With my lymph nodes refusing to shrink, we realized otherwise. The problem was, we had no idea how we would come up with thousands of dollars to pay for it. The price was less than a fourth of the cost of my chemo treatment, but my insurance would not cover it. We prayed earnestly for God to bring in what was needed.

Luke declared that he was going to earn the money that I needed to go to Mexico to get treatment. He put his seven-year-old brain to work and planned quite the elaborate "Luke's Lemonade for Momma" sale. He had his own lemonade recipe, and he chose two consecutive Saturdays for his event to take pace. He designed a flyer that Steve used as a template to create one on the computer. My young son walked in hot summer weather up and down the hills of our neighborhood and even knocked on doors to tell neighbors of our need face to face! Luke also asked Steve to take him to our local grocery stores so he could leave flyers on their bulletin boards. Each cup of Luke's lemonade would cost a dollar, and Luke declared that he would make enough to get me to Mexico.

I will never forget his response when we gently asked him if he knew how many cups of lemonade it would take to get me to Mexico. My momma heart didn't want my little boy to be sad if it took longer than he was expecting for me to get to go. Luke looked at me confidently and said, "One cup at a time, Momma. I'm going to sell one cup at a time. Remember, Momma, nothing is impossible with God!"

A whirlwind of miracles began. We were stunned. On the day of the lemonade sale, all of us except Luke were sick with an intense virus. I was going to cancel the sale, but a dear friend of ours said, "Lisa, don't cancel it. All we need is your driveway." Steve and I were too sick to do anything other than crawl to the upstairs bedroom window and peek out periodically.

One day I will meet the angels who stirred the hearts of countless people to come and support my son's efforts. God brought in four thousand dollars that day! The news station came. The local fire engine showed up and gave the kids attending the sale a tour of the truck. By evening the news station interview with Luke was all over local and national news. The next day the radio station, Yahoo! Parenting, the local newspaper, and the Ellen DeGeneres Show had all contacted our family. News went worldwide. My sister had started an online fundraiser for us earlier, and that was now all over the news as well.

Looks like Luke had it right. Nothing is impossible with God! Immediately donations came rolling in. I was on my way to Hope4Cancer!

Mexico

The virus that hit our family was so intense that Steve had to stay home with the children for the first couple of days rather than accompany me to Mexico. There was nothing easy about making the flight by myself, but God gave me surpassing peace the entire plane ride down. I was confident that He would send me the help I needed as I arrived at Hope4Cancer.

And help He sent. When the wheels of the plane touched down in San Diego, I learned that my sweet sister Lynnette was going to meet me there and cross the border to Tijuana with me. I cried happy tears. Then a message from Steve popped up on my phone that said "Check the fundraiser site." My jaw hit the ground as I saw that more than twenty-two thousand dollars had come in! God did that in less than two days. My body was physically tired, but my soul soared to new heights.

Despite traveling alone while recovering from a nasty virus, I was held by certain peace as I entered Mexico, as I was confident that God had led me there. Knowing this, I was set free to ride any waves of uncertainty with my eyes on my Savior. It made all the difference to know that I was right where I was meant to be in that moment.

Having Lynnette with me for those first two days at the clinic was a gift from God. She quickly learned the lay of the land and was an attentive and loving caregiver to me.

Sometimes my favorite memories came in the midst of tough moments. Lynn and I joked that we should have found another way besides cancer to take the sister getaway we had always talked about. But as the saying goes, it takes lemons to make lemonade.

We giggled together. We cried. We explored the boardwalk of Tijuana and walked by the waves of the ocean. I had been learning Spanish since my previous experience in Mexico and now tried to practice it with the locals. I had a long way to go before I could easily converse, but it was fun to interact more with the beautiful people. A smile could communicate love and kindness, even if I didn't quite understand what others were saying.

I love the Mexican culture. Mexican people value family, love, laughter, celebrations, work, and rest. This culture also flavored the clinic. The staff was caring, kind, and worked hard.

Steve arrived on the third day, just in time for our appointment with the head doctor. During our appointment with him, we had the chance to share our journey and hear his heart. We laughed, hugged, and even prayed together. To this day it remains the best doctor appointment I have ever experienced. We walked out of the doctor's office with a lighter step, renewed hope, and a sense of excitement for what Jesus would teach us during our time at Hope4Cancer.

We noticed how hard all the employees worked and the smiles they wore. The food served at the clinic was nutritious, artistic, and a delight to the palate. We loved the head chef, and in our home we still refer to him as the "king of sauce." The kindred hearts I met at the clinic became family for the month I was there. The treatments went up to twelve hours a day. They were non-toxic, but they caused some side effects from cancer cells being attacked. Numerous times we witnessed patients helping each other and caregivers encouraging each other. It was indescribably precious to witness and experience the love present.

One of the special doctors I met at Hope4Cancer was my functional medicine doctor. My appointments with him introduced me to the importance of considering the emotional component of a body not at ease, or in "dis-ease." God used him to help me recognize how intertwined physical and emotional traumas are with our overall health, such as my difficult birth experience with Gracie. Gracie is my joy bug and worth every bit of what I went through. But I did not understand that I had buried the emotions that had come with that experience. The Lord is my healer, and that includes emotional wounds.

My sister Laurie, who lived near us in the Pacific Northwest, was getting married the third week into my treatment. Our sweet

Ellie and Luke were the flower girl and ring bearer. The head doctor gave me the okay to take a two-day trip home in early September for the wedding. I praise Jesus for equipping me to make the trip.

I was thrilled to be there to straighten Luke's bow tie and fix Ellie's hair, to wrap them up and tell them how stunning they looked and how proud I was of them. It was a beautiful wedding from start to finish. My tears accompanied the couple's vows. It took my mind back to March 22, 2003, when Steve had promised to take care of me in sickness and in health. Buckets of joy ran down my cheeks as I shared in my sister's day.

I will never forget Ellie coming back down the aisle in her white flower-girl dress with a "cat that ate the canary" look on her delicate face. I had wondered if my shy one would make it down the aisle both ways. We had told her she could take her lovey, Diddy, an extremely worn and tattered bunny that she had had since birth. Steve had told her he would give it to her when she made it down the aisle to the front. I was at the back with Sammy J and Gracie as she made her return trip up the aisle at the end of the ceremony. As she sailed by me, grinning all the way, she showed me her basket, and there was Diddy tucked inside!

When Steve and I returned to Mexico to resume treatment two short days later, Luke went with us. It helped my momma heart to have him there. He had come for Steve's and my sake, yet we saw how Jesus shone His love and light to the patients, caregivers, and staff through this seven-year-old boy.

We returned home mid-September 2015 armed with everything we needed to remain on the clinic's home program. The recommendation was to wait two months and then get a non-radiation type of scan, such as an MRI, to see how my lymph nodes were doing. This would allow time for the inflammation from the initial treatment to subside.

Steve, Luke, and I left Mexico with hearts overflowing with precious memories and new friendships. One of the closest

Spirit-filled relationships I have today happened because I went to Hope4Cancer. My time in Mexico, evidenced by the fundraiser bringing in a total of thirty-seven thousand dollars, will always remind me that nothing is impossible with God. Nothing. I committed to pray "impossible" prayers more often.

Impossible Prayers from Scripture

I love how God uses my children and the Bible stories I read to them to remind me of truth. One night three-year-old Sammy J snuggled on my lap, listening to his bedtime story. I studied the picture of Joshua holding his hand out to the sun as I considered my prayer life. Can you imagine asking God to stop the sun from setting? Joshua did exactly that in Joshua 10:12.

Have you ever asked God for something but underneath been thinking, *There's no way*? Have you ever wondered if you had enough faith for a miracle to happen? Check out Abraham and Sarah in Genesis 18. Sarah laughed when she overheard the Lord telling Abraham that they would have a baby. She was no spring chicken! I would not classify Sarah's laughter as great faith. Despite her laughter, indeed she did have the baby the following year that God had promised. "Is anything too hard for the LORD?" (Gen. 18:14).

God wants two things from us: to believe "that he exists and that he rewards those who *earnestly seek* him" (Heb. 11:6, NIV). In Luke 18, Jesus told the story of a persistent widow to teach us that we should always pray and never give up! At the end of the parable, Jesus said, "Where will I find such faith when I return?" (see Luke 18:8). My husband's answer to this question early on in my cancer diagnosis was, "Here, Lord, *here*! We will pray and never give up!" He drew a picture of a cross with that verse, and it's been taped up in our bedroom ever since. When we pray in the Spirit through the written Word of God according to the will of the Father, we can keep asking and asking and not lose heart.

Faith that is seen is not faith. Faith is based on what is unseen. Hebrews 11:1 states, "Faith is the assurance of things hoped for, the conviction of things not seen." I can't see the wind, but I sure delight in the effects of the wind moving through the gorgeous maple trees outside my windows. I cannot see God, but I have seen and experienced the effects of His power at work. I know God exists. I know He is powerful beyond my imagination.

What stands out to me in Luke 1:37, "Nothing is impossible with God" (NIV), are the two words "with God." Hope springs from my soul, and peace settles the troubled waters of my mind. My heart pumps with joy. God's in charge, not me! Hope in self is misplaced hope, because hope in anything but God is destined to disappoint. Hope in God is hope secure. Because we have Jesus as our hope that doesn't disappoint, we can persist in praying, just as the widow did in Luke 18: "Jesus told his disciples a parable to show them that they should always pray and not give up" (Luke 18:1, NIV).

In the same chapter, Jesus was approached by a rich man asking how he could gain eternal life. This rich young ruler heard that he needed to sell everything and follow Christ. The crowd nearby exclaimed, "Then who can be saved?" We hear the promise again as Jesus answered, "What is impossible with man is possible with God" (Luke 18:26-27).

God is glorified by our belief in His power and ultimate control over every situation. Perhaps we have been in prayer for years for loved ones to hear Jesus calling their hearts to His. Our prayers have lost fervor as our hearts have lost hope. We have joined in with the crowd staring at the rich man's possessions, heads shaking, lips murmuring, "Impossible!"

Jesus set the example for us when He loved "to the end" (John 13:1). What we know about love is that it "always hopes" (1 Cor. 13:7). As we love with every breath, hope continues to fill every heartbeat.

God desires that we fully believe in His capability to accomplish His purpose in and through our lives. The Creator of the universe, who threw the stars into place, is not at all dependent on our performance to have His plan prevail. He is *God*! Believing that God can do anything He wants, however He wants, and whenever He wants prepares our hearts to see God's chosen miracles happen. The purpose for all miracles is God's glory. The Lord decides what each miracle looks like and when it happens.

The Mountain Becomes a Plain

I love the story of Zerubbabel speaking to the towering mountains of "impossible." Zerubbabel was governor of Judah when the Jewish exiles returned from Babylon and began rebuilding the second temple. Only the foundation was completed when opposition came and brought all the work to a halt. After seventeen years of silence, the prophet Zechariah was given this beautiful message from the Lord to deliver to Zerubbabel that flattened the mountain of obstacles ahead of Zerubbabel into a blessing-filled plain: "This is the word of the LORD to Zerubbabel: Not by might, nor by power, but by my Spirit, says the LORD of hosts. Who are you, O great mountain? Before Zerubbabel you shall become a plain. And he shall bring forward the top stone amid shouts of 'Grace, grace to it!'" (Zech. 4:6–7).

It's not natural for us to quiet our striving. When I was first diagnosed with cancer, I sought to learn as much as I could about lymphoma and what I could do for my health. I wanted to live long enough to kiss my husband's laughter-induced wrinkly face and snuggle our gray-hair heads together on our deck swing. I wanted to see my precious littles grow up, have late-night giggles together with them, and see them get married. I loved the thought of being called Grandma.

But striving didn't bring the peace my heart was longing for. Accepting Jesus into my heart had given me peace with

God, but living by His Spirit gifts me daily peace on Earth. Peace to accept hard. Peace becomes present when striving is absent.

We will all face mountains of impossibility. Our tender hearts are quick to want to fix what is broken. We move into bulldozer mode to attack the mountains in our way on our schedules. The word of the Lord from Zechariah to Zerubbabel is the word of the Lord to us today. We must trust God with our mountains and reap spiritual blessings as we watch God's grace demolish our mountains of impossible.

Regardless of the state of cancer in my body, I do not see mountains in front of me each day. I can shout to my mountain as Zerubbabel did to his, "Grace, grace to it!" (Zech. 4:7). I can watch the mountains of worry crumble right into those blessing-filled plains. For I know that the God who graciously authored a work to begin in my life will carry it to His intended completion without the help of my bulldozer.

Today I see Jesus through the eyes of my soul, but one day I will see Him face to Face. I love to inwardly gaze upon that moment when I will enter heaven's gates and look upon Jesus. When I see His majesty, His beauty, His power—it is then that my faith will be sight. I now see in part, but then I will see in full. Today is when we can exercise faith before it becomes sight. Trusting Him and believing in His power today to do anything He desires for His kingdom purposes intensifies the beauty of that moment when we will see Him face to Face.

It is our hope in Jesus Himself that makes all things possible today. The name of Jesus erases "impossible" from our vocabulary. No doctor will be slapping an "incurable cancer" diagnosis on me. I am not anyone's statistic. I am God's precious child whose days were numbered by Him before time began. A beautiful passage to visit when considering medical decisions is Psalm 139. I love to read this passage through several times in a row. We can let the truth of our days being numbered by God Himself lighten the burden we are bearing today. When we seek Him, He will tell us where to stop and rest. He called me to a cancer clinic by the ocean in Tijuana, Mexico. His hand held mine—and peace removed fear.

Behavior is determined by belief. Do our lives, our words, our love reflect the belief that nothing will be impossible with God? Have we made God as small as a cancer statistic? Does our behavior follow the belief that God can do anything, anytime, however He pleases? Do we believe that God will equip us for the paths He calls us to?

Lord, not by might, nor by power, but by Your Spirit! You breathed the heavens into place, and nothing is too hard for You!

When the Teacher
Is Quiet

The movie *God's Not Dead 2* shares the story of a teacher who is on trial for answering a student's question about Jesus. In a moment of despair, she cries out to her grandfather, "Where is God when I need Him the most?" Her grandfather gently reminds her that it is during a time of testing that the Teacher is quietest.

Our lack of *feeling* the closeness of Jesus increases our vulnerability to the enemy's attacks. Discouragement creeps in during these times when we plead and cry out to God and can't hear His answer or feel His presence. Discouragement settles like a dense fog that covers a windshield, removing our view of the blessings in our lives. Negative thoughts enter a chaotic spin cycle in our hearts. *I'm all alone. No one remembers me. Everyone is going about their normal lives, while mine has stopped. I am unseen. I am unheard. No one cares about me. Does anyone know how hard it is to raise up little kids in the midst of health problems?*

We can hear God's voice when we don't feel His presence in the place where He is never silent—the Bible. When the Teacher is quiet, we must use the textbook! The Bible is the very breath of God. It is God's living love letter to us, filled with promises from our God, who does not lie (see Titus 1:2). These are promises our souls can stand on no matter what our feelings tell us. God's Word holds everything we need for life and godliness (see 2 Pet. 1:3).

Scripture gives us numerous examples of men and women of great faith who battled through times when God seemed distant. My favorite one, which I mentioned in chapter 3, is about Job and his perseverance. Job's experiences teach me that my perception of God's proximity doesn't change the reality of His presence.

The Lord spoke to Job "out of the storm" (Job 38:1, NIV). He was right there in the storm with him. He is also in my storm, and He is in yours.

Steeping After Mexico

Being in hot water is uncomfortable, but tea steeps best in hot water. Beautiful treasures from God's Word seem to appear to me more frequently in the "hot water" seasons of life. Steve and I experienced some hot-water days while adjusting to being home after our month at Hope4Cancer.

In Mexico I was a cancer patient at a clinic I loved. Steve and I had time with the Lord, time with each other staring into the ocean waters, and a plan up on the wall for me to follow each day. I was surrounded by other cancer patients like me, and we shared the camaraderie of natural cancer treatments.

Then we reentered the orbit of home life. Children needed tending to, as did dishes, laundry, house cleaning, Steve's job, and a home healthcare program. Some brave souls entered into our bumpy transition to home healthcare, asking how they could help. My homeschooling group and my women's Bible study group provided help with the children, the house, and my heart. My dear friend Katie often adopted my four children into her days with her own four, giving them a chance to laugh and play together. I was amazed at the loving-kindness she displayed to my littles. My children were radiant after time spent with her. Katie, her husband, BJ, and their four children, Abby, James, Matia, and Bella, have shown us what the selfless, unconditional love of Jesus looks like. The friendship shared between our families is a special gift from God.

The Answer for Hurting Hearts

As we adjusted to our new normal at home, we enjoyed corresponding over e-mail with new friends I had made at the clinic. But October 2015 delivered pain to my heart when I heard news of precious friends going home to be with Jesus.

When my heart hurt deep, it was to my backyard I went. Our Northwest backyard had all sorts of huge trees with a deck off the upper floor where we could enjoy staring into nature. Sometimes when I experienced a day in which I did not feel I had a friend in the world, it helped to hang out with the chipmunks in my backyard. Giggles while watching squirrels were inevitable. Then I remembered who had made those squirrels. I looked up, smiled, and whispered, "Thank You, Jesus, for these creations of Yours that always point me to You."

All creation gives glory to God. At times like this, I need to be reminded of beauty. It comes in the flowers, the fall leaves, the smiles on my kids' faces, the hug of my husband. It's always there. Sometimes my tears blur it for just a moment.

I want for all to know His joy and His peace. I want everyone to know that when their hearts break, He knows where all the pieces are and holds each one. I close my eyes and imagine just climbing right up onto His lap, feeling His arms encircle me ever so gently yet ever so firmly, promising He isn't going to let go. And safe in His arms, I can pray for the heartaches around me through the strength He gives and entrust each loved one to Him. I can begin counting gifts again and return to peace and joy in believing that the best is indeed yet to come for all those who love Jesus. (blog post, October 30, 2015)

Turning Pages: Waiting Is Not Easy

Two months passed, and it was time to enter the MRI machine to see how my body was responding to treatment. Far worse than the time spent in the machine was the time spent waiting for the results of the scan.

Waiting. I smile now as I write that word, thinking of my little girls' impersonation of one of their favorite books. The children love the Elephant and Piggie books. One of the books is titled *Waiting Is Not Easy*. It's an excellent book for me as an adult! We frequently imitate Elephant and Piggie in our home. We will jokingly say, "And waiting is *not* easy!"

When my MRI results finally came, I recorded them in our family blog:

My kids as toddlers always love to be the one to "turn the page" in the picture books, delighting in the excitement of what will be on the next page. Sometimes they want to turn the page before I finish reading it! I'm not far off from that as a child of God. Sometimes I want to rush the pages and turn it to see what's coming next from the Author of life.

We received great news after the MRI! What remains of cancer is a 1 cm by .08 cm node. In fact, the radiologist said that if I didn't have cancer or a history of it, that lymph node doesn't even fit the pathological requirements to warrant a search for cancer in a healthy patient. In my case, however, it corresponds directly to the original lymph node that was the biggest, so we know it is cancer. But the size is small. My celebration has been real but quiet, partly from shock and partly from the questions that surround why I still have all this abdominal pain. Above all, I just feel completely in a state of thankful surprise, saying "Thank You" to Jesus over and over and over and over again. (blog post, December 1, 2015)

Praying as We Wait

"Elijah was a human being, even as we are. He prayed earnestly that it would not rain, and it did not rain on the land for three and a half years. Again he prayed, and the heavens gave rain, and the earth produced its crops" (James 5:17–18, NIV).

As a child, I attended Sunday school classes that taught me about Elijah. I saw him as a powerful and courageous man of God. He bravely took on 450 false prophets in front of a crowd. Elijah gave them all morning to call out to their false god, Baal, before starting his taunting. I loved this part of the story as a young child when Elijah started telling them to shout louder because maybe Baal was taking a nap, using the restroom, or off on a trip somewhere! I can only imagine how angry this made the 450 prophets working so hard to pray to Baal, only to receive deafening silence.

When the time came for the evening sacrifice and Baal had still not responded, it was Elijah's turn. He had the courage even during a major drought to have four jugs of treasured water poured all over the altar he would pray over—not one time but three. At Elijah's first prayer, God answered. And He answered *big*, leaving no room for doubt on where the answer was coming from. Fire fell from the Lord and not only burned up the sacrifice but the entire rock altar, soil, and water.

Looking at this one day in Elijah's life would make it easy for us to think that there is no way Elijah was a man "just like us." After all, his prayer called fire down from heaven!

But 1 Kings 17–19 gives a better picture of Elijah's life. We first hear from Elijah when he gives this message to King Ahab: "It's not going to rain until I say it will" (see 1 Kings 17:1). After he delivered that message, God instructed him to hide from the now severely irritated King Ahab.

Ravens supplied Elijah's daily food, and his water came from a brook. When the brook dried up, God told Elijah to go to a widow's house to be fed and cared for. This unlikely widow already had a son she couldn't provide for during this time of famine. She was preparing her last meal for her boy and herself when the man of God arrived.

My favorite four words in reading about Elijah's life are found in 1 Kings 18:1: "After a long time" (NIV). Elijah spent at least a couple years at the widow's house before God called him to deliver his next message to King Ahab. I wonder how God used this time of waiting to draw Elijah near and prepare him for the things to come. I wonder what questions went through his head when day after day passed without word from the Lord. Yet he prayed earnestly and obediently.

When the day came that God called him to act, Elijah was ready. It was time for him to pray for rain to end the drought. As he obediently and earnestly prayed for rain to come, Elijah kept

When the Teacher Is Quiet

his eyes expectantly on the horizon. Sure enough, God Almighty answered in the form of a small cloud in the distance. It's coming, Elijah; it's coming.

God may call us into seasons of preparation as He did Elijah. As we pray earnestly and watch the horizon, we are reminded that a cloud is forming. God is working, and He is preparing us to be vessels dispatched for kingdom work on His command. We joyfully serve our King until the day when another cloud will form on the horizon, and we will see the Son of Man coming "with power and great glory" (Luke 21:27)!

More Tests

Because the type of lymphoma I have does not have a good tumor marker test, it was time for me to consider having another MRI in the spring of 2016. Steve and I decided that I should first run a lab test that I'd had done in Irvine after my initial diagnosis to measure the amount of nagalase in my blood. Nagalase is an enzyme that increases in the presence of cancer or viral cells. The results came back two weeks later: the nagalase levels were significantly elevated.

We returned to God's throne room for marching orders!

Steve is my designated research specialist. He can look things up on Google and bring me only the necessary information to pray over, leaving behind all the stuff that would suck me into the black hole of anxiety and "what ifs." In January we had learned, through a friend's journey, of a home-based immune-system-building treatment from Canada called 714X. We had put it in our mental file of possibilities for future treatments. After prayer we made the decision to move forward with 714X injections, asking the Lord to use it to lower my nagalase number and improve my blood counts.

With a name like 714X, the treatment brought to my mind 2 Chronicles 7:14: "If my people who are called by my name humble themselves, and pray and seek my face and turn from their

91

wicked ways, then I will hear from heaven and will forgive their sin and heal their land." Context is vital when using Scripture to guide healthcare. We must look at who a passage was written to and consider the passage in its entirety. Although the words of 2 Chronicles 7:14 were spoken to Solomon after he built the temple and to the people of Israel, all Scripture has relevance for us today. The Holy Spirit teaches us what a passage says and how to apply it to our lives. When I look at how to apply 2 Chronicles 7:14 to my own life, I think of the importance of confessing sin that can dull my sense of communion with Jesus Christ.

Steve and I prayed before each self-administered 714X injection that He would heal us from any envy, anger, or bitterness trying to put roots down in our hearts. We prayed that as we were daily cleansed from sin, we would receive a fresh outpouring of God's Holy Spirit for the day. "The only hope of a decreasing self is an increasing Christ."[1] As self is emptied and Christ fills us, we walk a path of hope, joy, peace, and thankfulness, loving God and loving others through the power of His Spirit.

The elevated nagalase number, besides helping us decide to start the 714X, also confirmed my need for the MRI. To keep from increasing the load of toxins on my lymph system with radiation, we prayed for a local oncologist who would approve the use of MRIs rather than requiring CT scans to monitor me. The Lord provided a sweet European oncologist within one hour's drive of our home. After hearing our story, she gave her consent to my request to avoid further radiation from CT scans. The MRI was set for May 24, 2016, after I would have completed four weeks of 714X.

We also scheduled another nagalase test for the day of the scan. Because my elevated nagalase number could be due to either a virus or a cancer load, it seemed wise to us to get a new number to compare to what we would find on the MRI to help us make future decisions.

The night before the tests, I wrote in my journal:

Tomorrow I have a chest and abdomen MRI. Between a skin condition I had developed in February that was determined to be granuloma annulare, unstable energy levels, and an elevated nagalase number, I find myself pleading for the mercy of God.

Lord, because You are all powerful, I come asking for a miracle of healing. You are the Author of all miracles. I sense the exhaustion in Steve and myself. You are able to do exceedingly abundantly more than all we ask or imagine according to the power that is at work within us (Eph. 3:20). Jesus, it's not the size of my faith but the size of my God. It's not my name but the name of Jesus. I am coming, Lord, with full belief in Your power to heal for Your glory and Your kingdom purposes. My flesh cries out for healing, for full equipping and energy to parent the children. I pray that I would bring Steve good, not harm, all the days of my life. That my words would be life giving, filled with the Spirit. Lord, I know that You are in full control over every cell in my body. Let my life be a song that declares Your power, goodness, and glory to all. Please, Lord, protect our hearts. Be a shield around us.

I pray as I go to the imaging center for the MRI in the morning that Your peace would flood my soul, that Your gentleness in me through your Spirit would be evident to all, that Your hand would paint the results on the screen. I pray that Your light would shine through us. We are weak and at times feeling discouraged. Renew our minds and our hearts. Send us support from Zion and help from the sanctuary. Send Your angels to minister to Steve's heart, mind, body, and soul. Be the lifter of his head, God. Let him be set free from the shackles of this world and live intimately with You. Break our hearts for what breaks Yours. Keep our hearts free from selfishness, the enemy's lies, bitterness, discouragement, envy. Lord, these things are not from You. Let us be fruitful in the land of our suffering. Cultivate thankful hearts in us, Lord. Fill us to overflowing with Your joy. We need You, Lord. We cry out to You. Please give us a miracle. At the sound of Your voice, the enemy must flee. As we speak Your name, the enemy must flee. Be our fortress. I quiet my soul by resting in Your presence. (journal entry, May 23, 2016)

Trusting God in the Quiet

When God's voice isn't as loud as we are used to, when life as we've known it appears to be crumbling, our self-voice whispers to us that the grass is greener somewhere else. If only we had chosen that treatment or that clinic. If only our kids were older. If only we were retired with a nice savings account to pay for all the treatments. Regardless of what our emotions speak to us, grass is greenest where it gets the most water.

When the Teacher seems quiet, it's easy for us to get overwhelmed and confused. When those familiar clouds darken my view of God's incomparable greatness, I know it's time to go to my "most holy place." For me this quiet place to meet with Jesus is my prayer closet. I like to imagine Jesus sitting right behind me for me to lean back into His strong arms wrapped around me. Coming into the awareness of His presence enables me to pray in the Spirit. I open up His written word to Psalm 23 and start with the first four verses:

> The LORD is my shepherd; I have all that I need. He lets me rest in green meadows; he leads me beside peaceful streams. He renews my strength. He guides me along

right paths, bringing honor to his name. Even when I walk through the darkest valley, I will not be afraid, for you are close beside me. (NLT)

Praying Scripture is powerful and protective. Sometimes it helps me to keep my prayers to one or two words while I get my eyes to focus on Scripture. "Jesus, help!" is one I've used often, especially in times of decision making concerning cancer treatments while I'm in pain. "Spirit, come," and, "*Abba!*" are two other frequent flyers.

In early June 2016, we received the results of the MRI: "No evidence of disease"! We were elated! I ran down the middle of my street shouting praises to Jesus!

Our first appointment with my monitoring oncologist after the MRI was bliss. With kindness and happiness, she affirmed a totally clear chest and abdominal MRI. We tested for a nagalase number and received the lowest number back since the first test I'd had in 2014.

We remained on the home program from Hope4Cancer and also continued with the 714x injections, prayerfully walking step by step with Jesus. The two words that kept playing in my mind were "trust" and "obey."

Come Forth as Gold

Suffering is unpleasant. Yet the muck of difficulties here on Earth increases the glory we will experience when we arrive on eternity's shore. No hardship is pleasant at the time, but for those who are trained by it, we will reap a harvest of peace and righteousness (see Heb. 12:11). Job knew he was in a time of testing: "But he knows the way that I take; when he has tried me, I shall come out as gold. My foot has held fast to his steps; I have kept his way and have not turned aside. I have not departed from the commandment of his lips; I have treasured the words of his mouth more than my portion of food" (Job 23:10–12).

The children and I were traveling through U.S. history in their homeschool lessons and studying the California gold rush just as I was praying over Job 23:10–12. I read this from their history book:

Captain Sutter examined it carefully. He weighed it, pounded it flat, and poured some strong acid on it. There are three very interesting things about gold. It is very heavy, even heavier than lead. It is also very tough. If you hammer a piece of iron long enough, it will break into pieces; but you can hammer a piece of gold until it is thinner than tissue paper. You can hammer it so thin that you can see the light shining through it. Finally, if you pour strong acid on most metals, the acid will eat away the metal and the metal will change color. But if you pour acid on gold, it has no effect whatsoever. The shining nuggets stood all these tests. It was very heavy, it was very tough, and the acid did not hurt it. Captain Sutter and Marshall both felt sure it was gold.[2]

Trials are like a relentless hammer. Isn't it interesting that a person can hammer gold over and over and it won't break? Gold can be hammered so thin that light can be seen shining through it. Maybe this is why Job chose gold in sharing about his suffering. Hardships had hammered and hammered him; acid had been poured on his open wounds. But his faith in God was the real deal and would stand the test. He would come out as gold. The light of Jesus would shine through him.

My times of testing give me a chance to make deposits into God's treasury. My choices matter. How I respond to difficulties matters, every single time. Hard times are my chance to show the world how infinitely beautiful and valuable Jesus is. Every single time I respond with a sacrifice of praise in the midst of a hardship, it exponentially increases the weight of glory to come.

God always sees and hears us. Whether we are crying on our closet floors or feeling invisible in a sea of people, we are never forsaken by Jesus. Our home country has dispatched unseen forces under the Lord's command. Angel armies surround us!

Suffering is an invitation to us to participate in heaven's celebrations. Our choice to trust God through our tears brings shouts of "glory to God in the highest" (Luke 2:14) from the audience in heaven (see Luke 15:7). My soul eyes love to wander into God's throne room and catch a glimpse of the happenings there. Certainly everyone there understands what we sometimes forget—that it is only because of God's grace and power that we can say, think, or do anything that honors God. The inhabitants of the throne room are ready to do some fist pumps for our King the moment we choose thankfulness over self-pity, trust over doubt, and forgiveness over bitterness. It all matters—a lot.

The moment we enter heaven, we will see how our choices here mattered. But right now is when we have the chance for our faith to be faith. Imagine joining future kingdom celebrations that will result from our choices today. We can let our souls experience the joy of the celebrations happening now and allow the joy of the Lord to be our great strength (see Neh. 8:10).

Jesus, use our hardships to stir hunger in our souls. Give us a hunger for the great reunion with every beloved forever-family member that has gone before us; hunger for Your return; hunger to seek Your kingdom first; hunger to be set free from any sin that is entangling us and holding us back from taking that next baby step forward in the race You have lovingly marked out for us. I pray, Lord Jesus, that we would hunger to hold You as infinitely greater than anything here on Earth, even our own lives and the lives of our loved ones. Jesus, You are our very great Reward.

Happiness

One night as I was putting the babies to bed, my oldest stomped into the girls' room where I was, his arms filled with toys. Making trip after trip, he brought things from his room and dropped them in front of me. Soon I was surrounded by piles of clothes, Legos, Hot Wheels, and books. I watched as this tenderhearted six-year-old boy finally stopped transporting things and crumpled to the floor in tears.

"Momma, why am I never happy? You and Daddy buy me food. I have these clothes and a bed to sleep in. Just look at these things I have to play with! Why, Momma? Why am I never happy when I have so much?"

His seemingly out-of-nowhere outburst caught me by surprise. My first thoughts were that I had failed him. Or I wondered if perhaps his momma having cancer was causing him to behave this way. My thoughts exploded and turned my mind into a war zone. My tongue refused to work for moments that stretched into minutes as I held my sobbing son close.

"Lord," I prayed silently, "how do I point this precious heart to You? This sweet boy who put his faith in You as a four-year-old is hungering for more of You. I see Your Spirit stirring his heart. Give me the words, Lord!"

The Spirit brought to my mind 2 Corinthians 5:20: "We are therefore Christ's ambassadors, as though God were making his appeal through us. We implore you on Christ's behalf: Be reconciled to God" (NIV). The Lord spoke through Scripture: "We are not home yet!" We are ambassadors here on Earth, on a mission for our Master who is in heaven.

Luke's tears dried up as I finished tucking the girls into bed. I took him to the rocking chair, where he folded up his strapping little boy self into my lap. I said to him, "Sweet boy, we aren't home yet. We can delight in the blessings of these toys, but they will not give long-lasting happiness. We were created for fellowship with God, not for toys that break. In heaven we'll have amazing food, laughter, perfect relationships, and an endless eternity of delight. But most importantly, we will always be happy in our real home, because we will be with Jesus."

Any time I take a trip, I cannot wait to get back home to my own bed, my own food, and a sense of routine. If I've been away from Steve or the children, my longing for home increases all the more. In my real home in heaven I will not only come face to Face with my Savior and King, but I will be reunited with all my loved ones in my forever eternal family.

Ambassadors serve a purpose. They represent their own country while living in a foreign land. The most effective ambassadors understand their country of citizenship. The more we learn about heaven, the more joy our ambassador faces will reflect about our eternal home. Our real home is in heaven, and it will be anything but boring! Our excitement will spill out from our hearts and our lives as we seek to point others to their Savior and the home He has prepared for them.

Ambassadors here—citizens *there*!

Happiness on Earth

Though we are not yet home with Happiness Himself, we can experience happiness here. Because we have a pain-free joyous eternity with Jesus ahead of us, it would make sense for us to be the happiest people in the world. As a Christian, my life has a "happily ever after" promise.

Does this mean I should always feel happy? If not, what is wrong with me? Sure, I feel happy when I have good test results or a day of high energy. But how do I find that happiness when my circumstances are just not that great, when my prayers have not been answered the way I hoped? How do I feel happy when my body is filled with physical pain or when my emotional pain is a burden too great for a smile?

Randy Alcorn's book *Happiness* transformed my thinking. I grew up believing that joy was for Christians and happiness was for everyone else. The confusion I had regarding happiness for a Christian dissipated by the time I was through with this book. Through the word studies and scriptures presented in Randy Alcorn's book, my confusion regarding happiness in a Christian's life went from confusion to elation.

The happiness I have come to know is not the kind that causes a person to jump up and down the way a young child who is offered ice cream does. It's present even when circumstances are not favorable. It's a settled sense of a contented smile deep down in my soul. It's not unlike the kind of happiness my sweet girls experience as they count down the days until their birthdays. They are happy not because it is one of their birthdays but because they know their birthdays are coming. They are delighting in thoughts of baking a cake as they dream of the flavor of ice cream they will choose. They know their parents will have something special for them to unwrap. They are happy simply anticipating the joyful event to come.

Jesus has gone ahead to prepare a place for us at the grandest party we will ever attend! We will have endless gifts to unwrap as we explore eternity's shores with the One who is our best gift of all. Currently our lives are tainted with days of heartache and sadness, and we know happiness only in part. But one day we will know it in full, when Jesus returns and binds up sadness forever.

Fighting for Happiness

Happiness in the midst of trials is worth fighting for. Our eyes, if we give them freedom to do so, will naturally veer off course. Once our perspective goes, there goes happiness with it. Jesus is happiness. "Eyes on Him" brings a settled sense of happiness. When we begin to elevate any person or thing (including a cure for cancer) above Jesus, unhappiness will be rampant.

When unhappiness settles like a cloud of endless gray skies, we have a question to ask ourselves: "What is it that I am deeply desiring above all else?" In such times, as I sit with open palms, asking Jesus to shine a light into my heart, I begin to see what I had begun to pursue above Jesus. That's what sin is—elevating any person or thing above Him.

Jesus and happiness cannot be separated. True happiness is never found apart from Jesus. Any other source is a fleeting echo of it. Several times over the last five years a renewed desire to have all my health problems solved has popped up in me every so often. This desire has always been strongest when I have had an increase in symptoms. I have also recognized that any happiness I have felt over an improved test result has been short lived.

Searching for medical help is not sin. It becomes sin when my search for medical help becomes more important than my pursuit of Jesus. Happiness is found in living for God and others.

Time for a Survey: What Brings You Happiness?

Our family's celebration of my first NED (no evidence of disease) in June 2016 collided with the reminder that conventional oncology would continue to make guesses about how long it would be until cancer grew back and needed treatment. Steve and I chose to remain in full trust in the Lord rather than in man. Despite my skin condition and unstable energy levels, we were overjoyed that there was no visible cancer on that MRI scan.

In July 2016, Steve, Luke, and I returned to Hope4Cancer in Mexico. After my recent completion of Randy Alcorn's book on happiness, I was interested in what other cancer patients and caregivers looked to for happiness. During the few days we were in Mexico, I had a chance to ask people, "What makes you happy?"

A sense of kinship abounded through our conversations together on the struggles that accompany cancer. We discussed how fleeting happiness is; how job promotions, money, and success don't really satisfy. Of course we all agreed that we would be happy to see cancer gone for good, but living for this in and of itself did not produce happiness. Common to all patients was how our cancer diagnoses had caused us to take a good look at our lives and how we spent our time. One new friend shared how he had decided to live the rest of his life helping other people. He felt happy because he could help people! We hugged and laughed as we celebrated God's goodness in using the broken, *especially* the broken, to bring God's light and love to others. Through these conversations a common theme rang true: an inward focus did not produce lasting happiness. If we have breath, then we have the capacity to brighten someone's day.

Soaked Sponge: Information-Overload Unhappiness

Several times in my cancer journey an overload of new information swarmed us. Overwhelmed by what to do with all the possibilities for treatment, mental exhaustion shut down my capacity to think of even the first thing to do. Peace eluded me.

It's easy to mix up feeling overwhelmed with feeling unhappy. I had reached "soaked sponge" mental status, but the new information kept flying at me. I couldn't think straight.

It took years of experiencing this for me to begin to recognize what was happening. My information-soaked self needed to sit close to God's warmth so the Lord could absorb my confusion and restore peace. Now when I receive too many suggestions and ideas from healthcare professionals at once, I run to Jesus. He helps my mind empty out as He takes each question and concern. Sometimes it involves some uncomfortable waiting time, but He always shows me the next step to take. He is our rock and our fortress; and for His name's sake, He leads us and guides us (see Ps. 31:3).

Anxiety and Envy: Happiness Thieves

I often chuckle at the quote by French philosopher Michel de Montaigne: "My life has been full of terrible misfortunes, most of which never happened."[1]

This is so true of me! Some of what we worry about may come to be, but most likely a good majority of it will not. Anxiety rips happiness right out of us. The joy of today disappears when we try to take on tomorrow's "what ifs."

Envy is another happiness thief. I grieve my moments of being jealous of people who don't have health problems. I can even be jealous of people who do have health problems but have already raised their children. I can be jealous of people who have lots of money and can have whatever healthcare they desire. I can even be jealous of myself before I had cancer. I am truly chief of sinners! Only Jesus can rescue me from myself. I would be shoved underwater by the weight of medical decisions and health issues if I did not have Jesus to look up at.

Envy is a brick in the backpack we were meant to leave at the foot of the cross. God's grace helps us lay these bricks down and walk free from the weight of sin that so easily entangles. In Paul's letter to Titus, he states, "The grace of God has appeared, bringing salvation for all people, training us to renounce ungodliness and worldly passions, and to live self-controlled, upright, and godly lives in the present age, waiting for our blessed hope, the appearing of the glory of our great god and Savior Jesus Christ" (Titus 2:11–13). It is God's grace that has saved us, and it is His grace that trains us to say no to envy and yes to Him.

Happiness and Contentment: Needs Versus Wants

I am looking forward to talking to the apostle Paul about his letter to the church at Philippi. It is a letter so dear to me that I have sought to hide it in my heart. Paul gives us the secret to contentment in chapter 4 of this letter, where he tells the Philippians, "I have learned in whatever situation I am to be content. I know how to be brought low, and I know how to abound. In any and every circumstance, I have learned the secret of facing plenty and hunger, abundance and need. I can do all things through him who strengthens me" (Phil. 4:11–13).

Paul savored his relationship with Jesus more than food. Paul saw his hunger as a chance to treasure God's Word more than food. Paul's secret was his trust in Jesus living in him as being sufficient for every moment. Knowing that we have Jesus forever is the secret to contentment. Nothing else. All other hope is misplaced hope, gone in an instant. Jesus is hope secured. He is the secret to contentment, no matter what the scan results are or how many medical bills can be paid or how well our kids behave on any given day.

Coming to Jesus, our certain One, helps us discover what is unsettling our souls during a desert season. Perhaps we have made the mistake the people of Israel made: "My people have committed two evils: they have forsaken me, the fountain of living waters, and hewed out cisterns for themselves, broken cisterns that can hold no water" (Jer. 2:13).

Cisterns were storage tanks for holding rainwater. Choosing cistern water over creek water is choosing muddy water infested with mosquitoes over a nice glass of clear, filtered water. Trusting in our own strength is constructing our own broken cisterns. We will be left with empty tanks. Jesus is our never-ending fountain of living water, our source of sustaining strength.

I love singing hymns. Sometimes on a hard day I will belt out a hymn in the shower. When I do it really loudly, the kids giggle downstairs. The children love to have me sing next to them at night. It amazes me because my singing voice will be most appreciated in eternity when it is perfected by Jesus! One of our family favorites holds the key to experiencing happiness in our valley seasons: "Trust and obey, for there's no other way to be happy in Jesus but to trust and obey."

When we walk with the Lord in the light of His Word,
What a glory He sheds on our way!
While we do His good will, He abides with us still,
And with all who will trust and obey.

Trust and obey, for there's no other way
To be happy in Jesus but to trust and obey.

Then in fellowship sweet we will sit at His feet,
Or we'll walk by His side in the way;
What He says we will do, where He sends we will go;
Never fear, only trust and obey.

We were not created to live lives centered around self but to live lives centered around God. His love and happiness provide our perfect fuel. We jump up and down when we receive a positive lab result, but true, lasting happiness comes from anticipating the future secured for us with Jesus on the new earth.

"May all who search for you be filled with joy and gladness in you. May those who love your salvation repeatedly shout, 'The LORD is great!'" (Ps. 40:16).

Jesus is ours. We are His. *That* is happiness.

PART 2

Learning to Navigate

Change the Terrain

Our alarm clock in the early morning hours is often the pitter patter of Sammy J's feet running to my side of the bed for snuggles. I love pulling his warm self into my arms. Our family loves hugs. Our morning hugs are super tight, happy, long hugs filled with optimism for the day ahead. When I scoop up my big boy, Luke Daniel, I whisper into his ear, "I missed you all night long!" I absolutely love hugging my children. It warms me with gratitude from my head to my pinky toes. I'm certain my oxygen levels would visibly go up if I had a monitor on.

We have no control over the outcome of our life, only over the choices we make. God alone decides. One deep breath of this truth releases all pressure of thinking it's up to us to beat cancer. To be still and know that the Lord is God is a truth meant to free us (see Ps. 46:10). What a relief to know that *God* is God and we are not!

Here's what we *can* do: we can influence the terrain in our bodies and in our hearts while living surrendered lives. This means giving our best offerings to the Lord.

Proverbs is filled with wisdom, including tips for health: "A heart at peace gives life to the body, but envy rots the bones" (Prov. 14:30, NIV). Envy will negatively impact our health. A heart's terrain under the care of the Holy Spirit is kept free from harmful weeds of envy. Scripture also teaches us to take care of our anger before the sun goes down (see Eph. 4:26). Good medicine includes having a cheerful heart (see Prov. 17:22). Laughter feels good!

Other terrain changers include sifting, singing, adjusting diet, deep breathing, feasting on God's Word, and living Spirit-filled lives.

Terrain Changer: Sifting

Utilizing my "spiritual sifter" has been a helpful tool in changing the terrain of my body.

My husband makes scrumptious juice in the mornings. As he sends fresh veggies through our juicer and beautiful vitamin-rich juice fills the glass, a heap of fiber and things harder to digest are left behind in the juicer. Our hearts need the same "juicing" process in sifting through our daily texts and e-mails, opportunities, thoughts, and feelings.

Sometimes the messages we read send our thoughts into chaos resembling a washing machine stuck on a spin cycle! It helps to mentally place everything into the sifter: concerns, disappointments, fears, seeds of resentment, an agenda that feels too big, ministry opportunities, activities, and all our commitments. The sifter turns, powered by prayer, God's Word, and seeking the Spirit's counsel.

As we pray to God to create a new heart and renew a steadfast spirit in us, we will be changed spiritually, physically, and emotionally. All the negative components will remain in the sifter. Grace will freely flow out, bringing with it the Spirit's directives for each day. Leaving all else behind, we can breathe in and remember the grace given to us through Christ's death and resurrection. We can breathe out, allowing that grace that we have freely received to overflow to others.

The sifting process allows the heart to be set free from any doubts, discouragement, or unrest. The result? An ongoing fruit-filled life flowing out of a heart filled with surpassing peace.

Terrain Changer: Singing

Singing songs lifts the soul that is plagued by depression, anxiety, and discouragement. Singing gives me a chance to stop listening to my suffocating thoughts. Paul instructs us to be filled with the Holy Spirit, singing psalms and hymns and spiritual songs among ourselves, and making music to the Lord in our hearts (see Eph. 5:18-19). Sometimes when I can't squeak the song out, just listening to music with truth brings a little spring to my step.

Some of my favorite hymns to sing include "Jesus Paid It All," "Standing on the Promises of God," "Blessed Assurance," "It Is Well with My Soul," "Higher Ground," "What a Friend We Have in Jesus," "Trust and Obey," "Be Still, My Soul," "Great Is Thy Faithfulness," and "Be Thou My Vision." The Lord uses the words of these hymns to direct me into His heart of love and Christ's perseverance (see 2 Thess. 3:5).

Terrain Changer: Diet and Detox

After nearly five years of sitting in on discussions concerning what kind of diet one should eat for killing cancer cells, I have not arrived at one right answer. Should I follow a Paleo, autoimmune, FODMAPs, ketogenic, Hallelujah, low-oxalate, low-histamine, Budwig, anti-inflammatory, Gerson, or some other diet?

Steve and I have certainly tried most, if not all, of these diets. A chapter further into this book gives the specifics of the diet we choose to follow, which we have labeled the "Spirit-led diet." It's a prayerful, flexible approach to healthy eating. What is right for me will not be right for everyone. Our bodies are the living temple of God. What we eat matters, but food can quickly become an idol—something treasured above God. The Lord gently reminds me that when I said yes to giving my heart to Him, I said no to indulging in my flesh. "Those who belong to Christ Jesus have nailed the passions and desires of their sinful nature to his cross and crucified them there" (Gal. 5:24, NLT).

As much as we want to put good things into our bodies, we also need to get bad things out of our bodies. Exercise, drinking water, using a sauna, and other detoxification methods are all helpful for making our bodies less friendly toward cancer.

Terrain Changer: Deep Breathing

My difficulty increased in the summer of 2016. An abdominal wall injury that had begun after Gracie's birth had worsened over time. Our Medical Director answered our prayers for guidance with a surgery I had spent four years avoiding. We had been concerned about what major surgery might do to my abdominal terrain for cancer growth.

Thinking on God with God brought me gentle reminders of His self-existence and power that went beyond my limited human understanding. Surpassing peace accompanied the decision to enter surgery. The Lord tenderly cared for me, a lamb safe with her Shepherd.

The morning after my abdominal surgery, at 5:50 a.m., Steve received the phone call that his dad had gone to be with Jesus. Grief mixed with sweet fellowship as he sat beside my bedside in the hours that followed. Steve and I talked of his dad. We let our minds speak of what may have happened when he met the Lord face to Face.

Desire for Steve to be at the memorial grew within me. Doubts immediately harassed me. *How will I manage without him so soon after major surgery? How will I take care of myself, let alone the children, while unable to walk?* But amazing provision shows up in our most desperate situations. Our family and friends rallied around us! I smile from the memory of dear loved ones willing to brave my home in that time! Every need was met.

The hospital sent me home with an incentive spirometer, a medical device to exercise my lungs in my recovery from major surgery. The goal was to encourage my body to learn to breathe deeply again. Most of us breathe eighteen times a minute. The optimal number per minute is six deep breaths.

Just as deeply breathing oxygen brings healing nutrients to one's body post surgery, so too breathing deeply of God's Word changes the terrain of our hearts and renews our minds.

Terrain Changer: Feasting on God's Word

Steve and I first met on my fourteenth birthday in Huntington Beach, California. We have now been friends for twenty-six years, and yet even he cannot understand every war in my soul. After graduating high school, we went separate ways to college. During that time my friendship with Steve was cultivated by letters. Writing was how we got to know each other on a deeper level when we couldn't be together in person.

In the same way, Jesus has written us a letter—the Bible. By reading His words over and over again, we will deepen our friendship with Him. We can write letters to God by journaling responses to His letter. We can talk with Him through prayer. We can ask Him questions. We can grieve our sorrows together and share smiles during times of rejoicing. "Blessed be the LORD, who daily bears us up; God is our salvation" (Ps. 68:19).

We can nurture the terrain of our lives by feeding on the best food for our hearts, minds, and souls. We must feast often on God's Word, seeking first His kingdom. We must daily ask the questions, "Is Jesus my greatest treasure today? Am I loving God with all my heart, mind, soul, and strength today?"

Terrain Changer: Spirit-Filled Living

Each of us is a battlefield. Our flesh wars against our desire to walk in the Spirit. The power of living through the Spirit allows us to say *no!* to our flesh. Jesus died so that we could be free from the yoke of slavery to sin (see Gal. 5:1). When Jesus was preparing to return to heaven, He said He was leaving us a Comforter whose presence in us would be even better than Jesus staying with us! Wow! God is in me. God is in me?

It is only through the Spirit of Christ in us that we can live free from slavery to sin and experience the joyful freedom that comes from living in obedience to the Father. Being filled with the Holy Spirit is the most powerful terrain changer I know!

A. W. Tozer gives four steps to receive a fresh outpouring of the Holy Spirit:

First, . . . you must "set [your] face like a flint" (Isa. 50:7). . . . Say, "I go by the grace of God. I want all that the New Testament has for me."

Second, you must set your heart on Jesus Christ. Wherever He takes you, go with Him. Whatever He takes you away from, listen to Him and follow what He says.

Whomever you must ignore, move away from. If you want to be all that God wants you to be, set your face like flint and go straight to Jesus. . . .

The third thing you must do . . . is expose your life to God's examination. . . . Expose your whole life to Jesus Christ. Expose yourself in prayer. Expose yourself in Scriptures. Expose your heart in obedience. Expose it by confession and by restitution.

The fourth thing you must do . . . is to make some holy affirmations. . . . Declare before God never to own anything. . . . Another affirmation that has been important to me is to never defend myself. . . . Never defame a fellow Christian. . . . Never . . . receive or accept any glory.[1]

Resting in God's Control

Even in situations of filth, God will have His way with every human life. Esther Kim was a young woman imprisoned for her belief in Jesus Christ. She ate rotten food when she received any morsel at all. Her environment was completely toxic! No clean water in her dirty jail cell. Yet she lived. We see God's absolute control displayed throughout Scripture in stories like Paul surviving a poisonous snake bite in Acts 28:1-6. It's a hard but ever so freeing truth to remember that God alone sits enthroned over each of our lives.

Pursuing Jesus for who He is and not for what He can do bears the fruit of peace. I love taking a daily five- to ten-minute trip with Jesus. I close my eyes and fall back into His arms. Some days I climb up on the back of His white warrior horse. He does battle for me while I rest on His back. He takes me to a beautiful creek, where we sit listening to the water bouncing through the rocks. I am safe here with Him. He reminds me that He is in me and with me. My body is calm, my mind is quiet, my heart is joyful.

The best exercise we can do upon waking up each morning is to clothe ourselves with the Lord Jesus Christ and not think about how we can gratify the desires of the sinful nature (see Rom. 13:14). We ask the Lord to search our hearts and show us anything that does not please Him. We forgive others and seek to be forgiven. We release our hurts to Jesus, asking Him to cleanse our bodies from any envy, bitterness, or anger. No longer do I live for myself but for Him who died for me and rose again (see 2 Cor. 5:15).

I do not run this race for an earthly medal. Jesus is my great Reward! My prayerful decisions to deny myself certain foods that are known to cause inflammation or digestive issues in my body are acts of worship. My allegiance is not to any one particular diet or healthcare path; it is to Jesus Christ, the Son of the living God. "I have been crucified with Christ, and I no longer live, but Christ lives in me. The life I now live in the body, I live by faith in the son of God, who loved me and gave himself for me" (Gal. 2:20, NIV). My joy overflows not from choice of diet or healthcare but from seeking after Jesus, my greatest treasure. I set my face like flint as I run to Him, through His strength, for His glory.

Everything's Under Control

Humans love control. I am no exception. A certain specialized lab test done a month after my diagnosis reported a result that showed my cancer cells were "out of control." Discomfort grew as those numbers on the page pulled the stability out from under my feet. Unsettled, I groped for something to stand on.

The Bible provides unshakable stability in Jesus, who is never shaken by our whirling emotions. He pointed me to the story of Job and "creation's classroom."

Creation's Classroom

Job suffered, big. As with all Scripture, the book of Job is written to teach us, so that "through endurance and through the encouragement of the Scriptures we might have hope" (Rom. 15:4). Job is described as a blameless and upright man—one who feared God, shunned evil, and was called the greatest man among all the people of the East! Job was a prosperous rancher who had a wife, seven sons, three daughters, seven thousand sheep, three thousand camels, five hundred yoke of oxen, five hundred donkeys, and a large number of servants (see Job 1:1-3; 2:9).

Satan went to God and received permission to test Job, but Satan was not allowed to touch Job's life. Soon everything and everyone but Job's wife was destroyed. And his wife? Yikes! She urged Job to curse God and die! Job grieved in utter devastation, tearing his clothes. But in his crying out, he did not curse God. He chose through his tears to proclaim that everything he'd owned had been God's to begin with.

Job had friends who meant to be helpful. They weren't. As time went on, Job ended up asking his friends some questions. They responded with irritating answers. God took over the role of answering by asking Job His own questions as we enter creation's classroom in Job 38–42:

> Who is this that obscures my plans with words without knowledge? Brace yourself like a man; I will question you, and you shall answer me. Where were you when I laid the earth's foundation? Tell me, if you understand. Who marked off its dimensions? Surely you know! (Job 38:2-5, NIV)

> Have you ever given orders to the morning, or shown the dawn its place? (Job 38:12, NIV)

Do you send the lightning bolts on their way? Do they report to you, "Here we are"? (Job 38:35, NIV)

Who has put wisdom in the inward parts or given understanding to the mind? (Job 38:36)

Do you know when the mountain goats give birth? Do you watch when the doe bears her fawn? (Job 39:1, NIV)

Does the hawk take flight by your wisdom and spread its wings toward the south? Does the eagle soar at your command and build its nest on high? (Job 39:26-27, NIV)

To all this questioning Job responded, "I am unworthy—how can I reply to You? I put my hand over my mouth. I spoke once, but I have no answer—twice, but I will say no more" (Job 40:4-5, NIV).

The calm days of our lives paint for us a false sense of control. All it takes is one evening of listening to the news or one scan of the headlines on the computer to see the chaos around us. But while troubling events in our world can cause us concern, the story of Job teaches us that Satan is on a leash!

Only One controls the galaxies and each microbe in our body: the Lord Jesus Christ. He calls into existence something from nothing. Think on how every wave of the sea and every bolt of lightning is under His command. Ponder His character, mercy, grace, faithfulness, and love that abounds.

When Jesus walked the earth, He moved with compassion for the wounded. This is the very character of our God! He nestles us against His heart the way we do our own hurting children.

A determined focus on God's power diffuses our clouds of confusion. Job 23:14 promises us that it is Jesus who controls our destinies. Not cancer. Not any doctor. Trusting anything other than Jesus is misplaced trust and will result in chaos of the heart, mind, and soul. God's face is turned to us. He is in us and with us! I breathe in this truth, drop my shoulders, and exhale, "I trust You, Lord!"

Biblical Prayer for Healing

One of the extravagant blessings God brought into my life through the journey of cancer is my friendship with a dear pastor and his family.

In the fall of 2015, after I returned from Mexico, my momma sent me a link to a sermon series on the book of Job that her pastor was preaching. She knows me well! That first sermon had me worshiping through tears from my bedroom with my hands open: "Lord, You give, and You take away. Blessed be Your name" (see Job 1:21).

I was hooked! Powerful Spirit-filled preaching coupled with intense kindness and love radiating from this pastor's face had me listening by live stream to his sermons week after week. It became the highlight of my week.

In one sermon the pastor shared about his brother who had gone to be with Jesus at the age of forty-one because of lymphoma. I instantly understood more of the divine connection the Lord was orchestrating. I found a contact e-mail address at the church to share with the pastor my own lymphoma journey and appreciation of his Spirit-filled sermons.

In early September 2016, when my momma was visiting during my abdominal surgery recovery, she and I were sitting in my living room ready for the live-stream service to come on. We were shocked when the pastor looked into the camera for live-stream members, as he often does, and spoke a personal greeting to me! My momma and I looked at each other in joyful surprise before tears escaped down our cheeks.

The Lord is ever present in times of trouble. This was no exception. God sees us. God hears us. He is able to orchestrate more than anything we could dream up! That moment ignited an intense desire in me to meet this pastor and his family in person.

October 13, 2016, had me on a flight down to Long Beach, California, where this pastor and his wife lived! My excitement made it difficult for me to stay in my seat on the plane.

I am sitting at the Portland airport staring out the window, watching the rain fall. I sure love living in Portland! I am flying down to Southern California today for a four-day trip by myself. It's never easy to leave Steve (he is such a wonderful husband) or the children. I love them dearly. Yet this is a gift from the Lord to go. I am going to meet a most precious pastor and his wife tonight! Lord Jesus, would You grant us a wonderful time of encouragement, fellowship, a camaraderie of the cross, and a sweet time of prayer? Please fill all three of us with Your Holy Spirit, that Your name would be lifted high in their home tonight. I pray for Your Spirit to use Your Word to shine a light into the cracks of my soul, into any area of my heart that needs to be cleaned out, that I would be gifted deep communion with You, Father—to meditate on You with You, to meditate on the Word in the Word. (journal entry, October 13, 2016)

The Lord worked in ways forever etched into my soul in the home of the pastor and his wife that night. It was a struggle to pull myself away from the Spirit-filled fellowship when the hour approached midnight. My body may have been driving the car leaving their home, but my heart was still with them, soaring at the gift of eternal friendship.

It was the birth of a divinely orchestrated friendship that has been an encouragement to Steve and me numerous times since we first met. This pastor taught me what biblical prayer for healing was from James 5:13–16. All who are sick should seek to be prayed for by their pastor and elders in accordance with James 5:13–16. After the worship service at this pastor's church on Sunday, October 16, 2016, the pastor and the elders anointed my head with oil and prayed for endurance, equipping, and the healing of my body.

> 'Tis hard to recount on paper God's goodness yesterday. Indeed, the light of Jesus is shining in the darkness through the hearts of this church, and darkness will not overcome it (John 1:5).
>
> After a delightful time in my parents' Sunday school class, where the love of Jesus permeated the atmosphere, I had a life-changing moment in the prayer room.
>
> Tears flowed because of the love of Jesus. His love and His Spirit were there in that room. As I now read and meditate on Ephesians 1:15–23, it is quite applicable to my experience with Jesus and the church body today. Jesus is "far above all rule and authority and power and dominion, and above every name that is named," having full authority over all things to the church, "which is his body, the fullness of Him who fills all in all" (Eph. 1:21–23).
>
> I'm closing the door on saying "I can't do it" and opening the door to whatever God would do through an untrained girl who is a willing instrument for Him to play heaven's music. I am asking Him to clean out my temple from anything that prohibits His glory from being shown. This means I will have courage in Christ and trust Him to do His work through my willing and joyful surrender. I am closing the door to thinking any small thoughts of God and asking Him to daily increase His bigness as I seek to love Him with all my heart, mind, and soul.

There are higher heights and there are deeper seas, more souls to come into the kingdom, more hearts to turn to Him as their Healer, and more hearts to be set free from terminal sadness. I am hearing that some thorns of grace will remain. These thorns draw me to sit on His lap, firmly held by His love. By faith, God will turn these weaknesses to strength (Heb. 11:34). He will turn the thorns into shouts of victory in Jesus. This trip was a divine gift that will hug my heart and soul for years to come. (journal entry, October 17, 2016)

God has numbered our days and will bring us home to the Celestial City at just the right time. John the Baptist died in his thirties. My grandpa lived to be ninety-six, and he preached right up to his home-going! It's not about the number of our days; it's about living each day for God's glory. We are to delight in God moment by moment, His love filling every crevice and spilling over to all around us.

Knowing That He Is God

A dear sister in Christ sent me an e-mail sharing an experience of her husband. One night in his cancer journey, he woke up with a strong impression of the words from Psalm 46:10: "Be still, and know that I am God!" He had traveled through a lot of being "still" through days with surgeries, etc. On this particular night, however, it was the "knowing" part of this scripture that deeply impacted him. This man shared that knowing God was more than knowing that He exists. It was about experiencing Him and growing in intimacy with Him through the hardships of life. It was about surrender, awe, and trust.

My friend's precious husband is now in the presence of Jesus. He knows in full what we can now know in part (see 1 Cor. 13:12).

The word "know" comes up again in Romans 8:28: "We know that for those who love God all things work together for good, for those who are called according to his purpose." I've had a rocky journey with this promise when used out of context. It's important when claiming promises from Scripture not to pick the promise out the way a child removes only what he likes from the middle of a sandwich, leaving the bread on the plate. The top piece of bread teaches me that the Spirit is praying for me in accordance with God's will (see Rom. 8:27). The bottom piece reveals that God's purpose in all things is to make me more like Jesus (see Rom. 8:29). Looking at this promise in its entirety, "bread" intact, I declare, "I know that for those of us who love God, He is working every single situation in our lives for eternal good!"

To know and experience God as the One who sits enthroned over all is to know that everything in our bodies is not out of control but under His control. That changes everything. We can stop flapping our wings to get out of hard circumstances and imagine ourselves gliding through them instead. Eagles spend more time soaring than flapping. Our energy will be best spent feasting on God's Word as our source of strength. Jesus before us, Jesus behind us, Jesus carrying us.

On New Year's Day 2017, I wrote in our family blog:

> Does my behavior reflect my belief in an unchanging God, living with complete confidence on His unshakable promises found all throughout Scripture? Am I admitting my sin and stopping there? Or am I forsaking it? Is my greatest aim to please Jesus (2 Cor. 5:9)? Is my greatest delight Jesus Himself?
>
> Oh, to know God more, to wait on Him in all things, to experience Him more, to trust Him more, to love Him more. To start each morning surrendering my day to He

who inhabits eternity, knowing that He is God and enthroned over each circumstance in my day. I pray that the stillness of my soul comes not from life's circumstances being okay but from remembering how great my God is. Isaiah 30:15 says that in returning and rest is my salvation, in quietness and trust is my strength.

The beautiful hymn below, "All the Way My Savior Leads Me," was written by Fanny Crosby. I pray with each passing day until our Jesus returns again that He will make me more like Him. That I will know and that my life will show that all the way my Savior leads me.

> All the way my Savior leads me;
> What have I to ask beside?
> Can I doubt His tender mercy,
> Who through life has been my Guide?
> Heav'nly peace, divinest comfort,
> Here by faith in Him to dwell!
> For I know, whate'er befall me,
> Jesus doeth all things well,
> For I know, whate'er befall me,
> Jesus doeth all things well.
>
> All the way my Savior leads me,
> Cheers each winding path I tread,
> Gives me grace for every trial,
> Feeds me with the living bread.
> Though my weary steps may falter,
> And my soul athirst may be,
> Gushing from the Rock before me,
> Lo! a spring of joy I see,
> Gushing from the Rock before me,
> Lo! a spring of joy I see.

All the way my Savior leads me;
Oh, the fullness of His grace!
Perfect rest to me is promised
In my Father's blest embrace.
When my spirit, clothed immortal,
Wings its flight to realms of day,
This my song through endless ages:
Jesus led me all the way,
This my song through endless ages:
Jesus led me all the way.

Jesus is my guide, always present. Not one single circumstance has come my way that has been a mistake. While everything is not under my control, not one single cell in my body is outside His control. He alone is "the upholder of my life" (Ps. 54:4)!

Missing Skin: Relationships and Suffering

am a sensitive soul. If you tell me your arm hurts, mine starts aching. It's both a blessing and a challenge. God has purpose in the way He uniquely designed each of us, including my extra-charged nervous system.

My cancer diagnosis took off the outer layer of my "skin," leaving me raw, vulnerable, and reactive. I have at times pulled up a chair to my own pity party of one. I've had sob sessions on the floor of my closet, where Jesus has been my ever-present Friend to cry with. Disease and chronic illness disrupt normalcy.

The energy that was once present in me to put into relationships dwindled with each passing month.

The loss of the normal flow in life can tempt me to become bitter. Bitterness is a sneaky poison. When I give in to thinking about myself more than about God and others, it results in an inward focus and creates a perfect recipe for a hardened heart. Asking the Holy Spirit to do some gentle cleansing in my heart helps root out the seeds of bitterness before they have a chance to sprout.

Recognizing My Need for Others

With four young children to tend to alongside our cancer journey, Steve and I were grateful when so many people came alongside us to help. We hung onto every kind word, hug, financial gift, play-date for the children—even an oil change for the car! But slowly the e-mails, texts, cards, and offers of help began to dwindle as the sprint became a marathon. We knew we needed to do better at voicing our needs, but we battled with not wanting to trouble anyone. We had been needy for so long!

I have never been good at pretense. Just ask the high schoolers of the youth group Steve and I helped lead after we were first married. When we played card games that involved deception, they said, "Lisa, uh, you can just sit this one out!" We all had a good laugh, but they were right! I could not deceive anyone! One look at my face, and they knew if I was kidding or serious. Real life is the same for me. If you ask me how I am doing but you haven't seen me in a few weeks, I won't know where to start. If Steve is next to me, he rescues me in these moments with truthful and gracious answers!

Our emotional energy when out in public grew low from the physical toll our home life was taking on us. We showed up at church with nothing to give, looking for arms to collapse in.

Towering waves of discouragement crashed over me after I had toe surgery in the fall of 2016. I'd had a bone spur sticking straight up into the nail bed. I went into that surgery ill prepared. After all, it was just a toe!

I had unexpected complications, resulting in my foot being balled up like a clenched fist, unable to be used for days. I crawled around my house in tears. I wanted people to burst through my front door and just truly know that I was a mess. But I never asked for help. God used that week to break me, bind me, and shine a light on people who were available to help my family. I asked Him to make me brave, to help me pick up the phone and call when I needed someone to be my "moon" when all was dark. This was reminiscent of a blog post I had written earlier:

> Tonight Steve and I took some camping chairs out to the deck for a dry spot to sit and enjoy the quiet night. What we noticed was how bright it was out tonight. We looked behind the house to see the reason why and saw the beautiful full moon lighting up our backyard. When I walked back in the house, I was heading to bed. But as I turned to head up the stairs, I looked up at the window in the hallway and saw that mesmerizing full moon lighting my way again. I thought of John 8:12, the verse we've been memorizing with the kids for homeschooling: "I am the light of the world; whoever follows me will not walk in darkness, but will have the light of life" (NIV).
>
> Beyond the challenges we've had around here the last few days, my heart has ached for the hard things going on in loved ones around me. Waves of ache have hit dear loved ones. We have talked in our school time this year about how the moon reflects the light of the sun the way we can reflect the love of the Son, Jesus. But tonight, as Steve and I sat in the moonlight and prayed, it just struck

me how the moon can completely light up a dark night so beautifully and so quietly. Sometimes when the hard gets really hard, light feels so far away. Steve and I have felt that at times. I am always thankful for the people who have been willing to sit in our mess with us with a hug, reflecting the light of Jesus into our dark, not with "right answers" but just their presence. (blog post, October 26, 2015)

To My Suffering Friends

In pondering the previous five years in which I have cycled between hardship and moments of reprieve, I recognize a pendulum pattern, going from discouraging days that are the lowest of low to spiritual tank-filling days that are the highest of high. God has used both the spiritual fillings and times of dark discouragement to teach me more about Himself, His love, and navigating relationships in the midst of chronic illness.

To my fellow suffering friend, here are some gems Jesus has taught me through my mistakes in times when I have needed help. May they encourage and equip you!

1. Choose to be vulnerable. This is tough. This is really tough. If we do not choose to be vulnerable with others, it is possible they will mistake our "strong faith" for a lack of need. Most of the time, this couldn't be further from the truth.

2. Ask God each time you walk into a room to fill you with His love for everyone in the room.

3. Refuse to keep a record of wrongs (see 1 Cor. 13:5, NIV). When people's words are hurtful, remember that most often the words are coming from a heart of love, even if they don't transfer that way. I remind myself

of my sensitivity, which plays a role especially in how I interpret written communication. Jesus prayed at the cross, "Father, forgive them." In the book of Acts, Stephen prayed the same when he was being martyred. How much more should I imitate Jesus?

4. Remember that you too are a sinner. I like to remind myself that I am "chief of sinners" (1 Tim. 1:16). Some days this is a reminder I need when I get critical of others.

5. Teach people how to come alongside you in a way that is helpful. Sometimes people want to help but aren't sure what would be helpful. It helped Steve and me to come up with a list of specific needs to share with the loving helpers whom God sent to us.

6. Take time to respond to hurtful comments. As tempting as it is to quickly hit "Reply" to an e-mail message that missed the mark of its writer's intention, take at least a day before you respond. Written communication is tough when interacting with people in pain of any kind. It helps in these moments to turn off the cell phone or laptop and sit with Jesus. I ask Him to tend to my hurt and set me free from the sin that easily comes after hurtful words. Jesus helps me to start praying for the sender, praying God's richest heavenly blessings. I ask Him to remind me of my own sin being greater than all and to remember that not everyone is called to have me be the focus of their lives. It's so easy to start feeling entitled when we hurt for a long period of time. Holding onto any hurt will render us unfruitful for the King. By taking a day to pray, Jesus can transform our hearts and vision so we can see what was really being said and that it was wrapped up in love.

7. Ask God to be your outer layer of skin each morning.

8. Ask God to show you one thing you can do to encourage the people who have come alongside you. Resist the tendency to turn inward with your focus and ask God to help you live for Him and for others.

9. Go first to God's throne, not the phone. We can place expectations on those we love to comfort hurts that Jesus wants to tend to Himself. Oh, how He loves us! Jesus is especially good at absorbing my spin-cycle thinking as He lulls me to stillness with His gentle whispers, "I see you; I hear you; I am here."

10. Take a good, long look at the cross every morning. The cross reminds us how much Jesus loves us and that all suffering is temporary.

Help for the Caregivers

Choosing to come alongside a hurting heart is a beautiful, courageous act of love. This choice comes from a heart that wants to follow in the steps of the One who, over and over again, chose the broken people. As Steve and I have been lovingly tended to by people who have chosen to co-suffer with us, the list below reflects actions that have been encouraging and helpful for us and gives us examples of how we can extend the same love to others.

I pray that something on this list will encourage and equip you in your own situation and give you tools for reaching out to others around you who are hurting. May you experience a deep-down leap of desire from Jesus Himself to lay up treasures in heaven by your own sweet, sacrificial love. Your sacrifice will be a pleasing aroma to God and will be rewarded one day when you meet Jesus face to Face.

1. Use words that build up (when in doubt as to what to say, use an emoticon when texting). Below is a list

of life-giving statements that people have shared with Steve and me over the last five years—powerful, wonderful, truthful, loving words that have been expressed through written communication such as texts, e-mails, and cards. I love to record messages from others that will restart my Ferris wheel when I am stuck at the bottom by despair, discouragement, and doubt:

- "Prayers rising."
- "How can I best walk this with you?"
- "My heart is aching right now."
- "I am sorry for your hard."
- "I'm locking arms with you."
- "On my knees now."
- "Interceding at the throne for you."
- "Holding onto Jesus with you and for you."
- "Praying for your heart to be held."

2. Be brave. Go beyond the gift of praying for people. Give the sacrifice of being part of the help they so desperately need. Ask the question, "How can I help? Tell me one thing I can do for you this week." Ask them to teach you how you can best come alongside them. Ask what they find to be encouraging.

3. Choose to give a hug and say, "It's so good to see you," instead of asking, "How are you?" If you have time to hear how they are doing, ask a specific question. "Has your nausea improved at all?" "How has your energy level been this week?" "How is your heart?" "How is your spouse holding up?" "Has your sleep improved?"

4. Let the person who is suffering know that you are thinking and praying for them. Assume that no one

else has sought to do so. We have had people tell us they have been praying for us for a year. That is such a gift! But the gift would have been multiplied if we had known that they were praying for us that entire year! Little notes and messages are an amazing boost!

5. Set a reminder for anniversary moments in the sufferer's life. For example, the day a spouse went to be with Jesus or the day of the person's diagnosis. Be intentional about sending your friend some form of encouragement for those days.

6. Above all, validate, validate, validate. Validate the hardship without comparing it to any other situation you have ever been in. Suffering is not a mystery to be solved but an invitation to sit by a hurting heart. The most encouraging moments I have had are when someone scoops me up in a big hug. No words, just simply two arms filled with love to share, two ears with time to listen. So often it is a big bear hug, not a sermon, that a wounded heart is hungry for.

Loving Boundaries

Cancer set me free from overloaded schedules. I now want to run the other direction when too many commitments come up. Looking at a calendar that allows for our "flexible routines" brings me peace. This has gifted us ample family time together, including pajama mornings, hide-and-go-seek, unhurried family dinners, and giggly bedtimes. The children do better when they are not involved in too many activities at once. We love options like rock climbing and biking that allow us to take them when it's a good day instead of at a set time each week.

At my local Bible study, our teacher included a story about how we are either a flower pot or a pressure cooker. I spent most of my life in the category of a pressure cooker, following the example of Martha in the Bible who served and kept things running smoothly. When I was a kid, I used to put "brush my teeth" on my to-do list just so I could experience the thrill of checking off the box.

Incoming: cancer! No longer was I able to keep up with my pressure-cooker self. Over time God transitioned me to being a flower pot. It was not by my choice that I was transitioned but by His loving boundaries that He began to place around me. Most days I am grateful for the quieter life God has given me. He has used trials to teach me more about Himself and about relating to other people. By praying over the relationships that God has directed me to invest in, my world has become a little smaller these last five years. But also in many ways my life has become richer. My sense of community has exponentially multiplied. I have been prayed over, cried with, and checked on. The enemy is one-upped as we avoid the traps that come with an inward focus, and the sufferer and co-sufferer choose to be vulnerable together.

Jesus is with us always. We have His Spirit within us and His body around us. The members of our forever family, the church, are His eyes, His ears, His hug, His hands, and His feet to one another. I love the story from the Gospel of Matthew about the blind men who were calling out to Jesus:

> As they went out of Jericho, a great crowd followed him. And behold, there were two blind men sitting by the roadside, and when they heard that Jesus was passing by, they cried out, "Lord, have mercy on us, Son of David!" The crowd rebuked them, telling them to be silent, but they cried out all the more, "Lord, have mercy on us, Son of David!" And stopping, Jesus called them and said, "What do you want me to do for you?" They said to him, "Lord, let our eyes be opened." And Jesus in pity touched their

eyes, and immediately they recovered their sight and followed him. (Matt. 20:29–34)

These men were quieted by the crowd, but Jesus stopped for them; He didn't pass them by. He won't pass by us either.

Lord, let me be one who stops, one who asks, "How can I help you?" In my pressure-cooker seasons, let my hands be Your hands as I seek to lift physical burdens from my forever family. In the seasons that hold more flower blooming and less dishwashing, give me deep contentment of the soul. Whisper often to me. Remind me that I am Your vessel. Let me be a channel of Your love and light through my words and my hugs. Amen.

When Life Tastes Like Gravel: Seasons of Lament

O n the day after Thanksgiving in 2016, unexpected grief came over me:

A surprise wave of tears has come over me this morning. Today is three years, to the day, since cancer entered the pages of my journal. This morning while gathering up the children to decorate our home for Christmas, I felt grief rather than happiness. Confusion and frustration settled in like storm clouds. A pep talk to myself ensued: "Why is my heart so sad? I'm still here! I should be praising Jesus for what I've been given—three years of life since cancer entered the picture!"

As my tears are falling, I am realizing I never grieved being diagnosed with cancer. Grieving to me was something reserved for someone's death. Someone asked me once if I had taken time to grieve what has been lost through my cancer diagnosis. I thought, "Why would I do that when God has richly blessed me with so much in the midst?" (journal entry, November 25, 2016)

I had met a dear friend on my recent summer trip to the clinic in Mexico, and she had become one of my safe places to go when my emotional wounds started talking. When I talked with her, a cozy warm blanket wrapped around the parts of me that hurt the most. She pointed me to Jesus as she shared my sorrow.

I sent her a message during the time of my third "cancerversary":

It's a fight for my perspective on this day, November 25, 2016, ever since 11/25/13. It was at 3:35 a.m. on the day I was in the ER room with Steve and my four-month-old baby Sammy that I first heard the word "cancer" regarding my abdominal pain that I had been having. They had to admit me immediately and separated me from Steve and baby Sammy, who I was nursing often. Stunned into silence, Steve and I said a surreal good-bye as I was wheeled down the cold hospital halls, further and further away from my little baby and my husband's strong arms. When I arrived at my room for the night, I found I was put into a suffocatingly small sectioned-off part of a shared room. The other patient had late stage cancer and was angry. The bathroom was shared, and it had her personal measuring device for urine that happened to be overflowing. I could not use the bathroom, and I lacked the courage to buzz the nurse's station. I've struggled with not wanting to "be a bother." They had written LYMPHOMA in big red capital letters on the whiteboard next to my bed. That has forever been brand-ed into my mind. My milk was filling up steadily, and I had no baby and no pump. I watched the clock tick to the words cancer . . . cancer . . . cancer . . . for over an hour before I found myself desperately searching the ceiling for other thoughts to fill my mind. It was in that moment, right there in my part of a hospital room, that I felt an an-gelic presence fill the room. Psalms started to push back the cancer thoughts. I jumped straight from shock to, "I will walk this for *You*, Lord."

Three years after my diagnosis, I realized that this was all the processing I had done. Within twenty-four hours I had re-solved not to let Jesus down. I had squelched the thoughts of grief about cancer entering into my family while my kids were so little. It seemed almost unspiritual to me to so indulge in heartache. *How can I possibly experience grief when I am still here?* I thought. *I have a wonderful husband, four healthy kids, a home, two cars that work, and enough money each month to pay the bills. What is my problem?*

Until our coming One returns and binds up sadness forever, we will travel through seasons of sadness. I shrunk back from Christians who tended to "toss a tambourine" at me during times of sadness. I did need their reminders to "keep singing, Lisa, just keep singing," and they were all sweet, loving people. But some-times what I needed first was a long squeeze hug. They were right that we should always bring the sacrifice of praise. What is also right is to allow ourselves the time to tell Jesus all about it with-out skipping how we feel about the sad parts.

Lamentation

God used my worn copy of *The Horse and His Boy* to teach me that Jesus wants me to express my sorrow. This third book in the

C. S. Lewis series *The Chronicles of Narnia* tells the story of an orphan boy's journey to his original homeland. My weary body resonated with the boy, Shasta, as he dropped down in exhaustion:

> Being very tired and having nothing inside him, he felt so sorry for himself that the tears rolled down his cheeks. What put a stop to all this was a sudden fright. Shasta discovered that someone or somebody was walking beside him. It was pitch dark and he could see nothing. And the Thing (or Person) was going so quietly that he could hardly hear any footfalls. What he could hear was breathing.[1]

He could hear Him, but he could not see Him. When Shasta gained courage to ask who was there, Aslan's answer was, "One who has waited long for you to speak."[2] Aslan went on to encourage Shasta to share all his sorrows. Later in the story, when Shasta was traveling back through that same pass, he realized that Aslan had been walking on his left side to protect him from falling off a steep cliff that he hadn't known was there. Aslan, always present, always in control.

Aslan, our Jesus, wants us to speak. Aslan knew better than anyone the twists and turns Shasta had navigated! But Shasta needed to release the internal pressure building from holding his sorrow inside.

I don't like grief, because the wounds bleed, and I can't find the bandage that fits. What do we do when life tastes like gravel?

Jeremiah the prophet has an answer to that. The biblical response to seasons of chewing on gravel is lamenting. Lamentations 3 is a safe haven for grieving hearts. Jeremiah describes himself as "the man who has seen affliction" (Lam. 3:1). He has forgotten what happiness is; his endurance has perished and so has his hope from the Lord. He calls his afflictions "worm-wood" and "gall" (Lam. 3:19). Jeremiah's teeth are grinding on gravel (see Lam. 3:16).

This is really in the Bible—a man of God expressing inner-most tumultuous thoughts! Lamenting is both recognizing and expressing. It is okay not to be okay!

Our lamenting can be private, with trusted friends, or even public. We can lament through the book of Psalms, praying David's laments out loud.

Lamentations 3 teaches action steps to complete the lament-ing cycle. When life hurts the most, my thoughts will spin out of control if I do not call to mind these eight things:

1. The Lord's love is steadfast love.
2. The Lord's mercies never end.
3. God equips us anew for each day.
4. God's faithfulness is great.
5. God is my portion—Jesus is always enough.
6. We can put our hope in God.
7. God is good to those who wait for Him.
8. We must wait quietly for the salvation of the Lord.

My own tiny taste of grief also stirred up a hunger in me to learn how to walk by others who have been deeply wounded by loss. Questions spun in my mind: How do I walk with other Christians through a season of grief? Am I trying to hurry them through grief because I desperately want them to feel better? Does it make me uncomfortable when their sadness is so great and I am powerless to fix it? How can I ache so deeply with them yet have words com-pletely elude me?

Grief can look so different from one person to the next. It is unique to come across someone who is completely at ease along-side those who are grieving. Silent companionship is priceless in rock-bottom valleys. My cancer journey has provided us days of sweet privilege sitting by special friends in times of grief in the midst of our own suffering.

Our Burden Bearer

When I was a young child, my Sunday school class often sang the hymn "What a Friend We Have in Jesus." I've noticed when studying the stories behind most hymns that painful experiences sparked truth from God's Word into these powerful and life-altering songs.

This is true of Joseph Scriven, the author of "What a Friend We Have in Jesus." His first fiancée died in a tragic drowning accident the night before their wedding. He left his home country of Ireland to get a new start in Canada, searching for something to fill his empty heart. His second fiancée passed away from tuberculosis before their wedding.[3]

Sadness is a crushing burden to carry. Scriven's trials propelled Him into the arms of One ready to lighten his load. "The LORD helps the fallen and lifts those bent beneath their loads" (Ps. 145:14, NLT).

These first and last stanzas of "What a Friend We Have in Jesus" reflect Joseph Scriven's desire to be in sweet fellowship with his Savior:

What a friend we have in Jesus,
All our sins and griefs to bear!
What a privilege to carry
Everything to God in prayer!
O what peace we often forfeit,
O what needless pain we bear,
All because we do not carry
Everything to God in prayer!

Blessed Savior,
Thou hast promised
Thou wilt all our burdens bear;
May we ever, Lord, be bringing,
All to Thee in earnest prayer.
Soon in glory bright, unclouded,
There will be no need for prayer—
Rapture, praise, and endless worship
Will be our sweet portion there.

After years of sharing his love of Jesus with others, Scriven became ill. A friend noticed this poem that Scriven had written thirty-one years earlier lying by his bedside. When asked if he was the author of this beautiful poem, his answer was, "The Lord and I did it between us."[4]

In seasons of lament, we have One who is ready to be our burden bearer so we can be His image bearer. Through lamenting we move a step closer to heart and soul healing. We avoid loosely sticking a Band-Aid on our wounds, trapping all sorts of hurt so it can fester. We cry out to Jesus with Jesus. He experienced sorrow, grief, loneliness, abandonment, and death. He is big enough to handle our questions when they come. He is patient enough with us, when frustration wells up into a tantrum, to lovingly hold us quietly through it.

Jesus desires to bind up our wounds, holding the broken parts together in His Healer hands. In my journal, the day after Thanksgiving 2016, I began taking active steps in calling to mind God's faithfulness to me through our cancer season:

My children, who were four months, one year, three years, and five years old at my diagnosis, are out there decorating my house for Christmas. I hear happy feet and laughter with the occasional (or sometimes frequent) sibling squabble on where to put things this year. Those little feet are growing every day! Steve has a job that allows him to work from home often. Steve has learned how to cook amazing food! He is a constant example to me of the steadfast love of Jesus in how he serves our family. I am sure the applause of heaven is often louder because of God at work in Steve. He is a bush not burned, sharing the light of Jesus to all as people wonder how he keeps going (Exod. 3:3).

That beloved and tender friend I told you about at the beginning of this chapter knew grief all too well. We had a sweet-to-my-soul sharing of hearts over texting that ended with a sacrifice of praise from her: "We love you—we don't understand any of it, but we love you, and we're sticking with that!" Her love for Jesus was rock solid amidst her grief. I saw her living out Lamentations 3, her trust rising in a sweet aromatic offering to Jesus. She taught me about bringing our laments back to praise for Jesus, who took on human form and died on the cross. His death and resurrection are our guarantee that all seasons of lament will indeed have a final good-bye at His glorious return. He is coming!

Heaven is watching. Jesus is holding. Angels are ministering. We are always seen, we are always heard, and we are never alone.

Lord, show us how to be vulnerable and weak around God's family. Teach us how to lament in a way that brings others to know You. Give our friends and family insight into the truth that we have hurts that still need hugging. The strength they see in us is Your strength in our weak vessels. Thank You for the friendships You have birthed through adversity. We need You badly. Thank You for the way You tend to our hurting hearts and bind our wounds. We love You, Lord, and we are sticking with that! Amen.

Cancer and
My Littles

My children are my tender spot. I never considered the possibility of not being the one to raise them up into adulthood. In all my anxious thoughts I had as a young mom, my death never made the worry list.

My first Christmas with cancer came forty-eight hours after diagnosis. I numbly watched the older three open gifts while I held baby Sammy. My brain was stuck on one question: "Is this our last Christmas together?" Cancer was new. Cancer was loud. Thoughts of what might lie ahead stole the "merry" out of Christmas.

Facing the unknowns of cancer has radically changed the way I parent. Some nights exhaustion still dictates the type of bedtime routines that occur; Steve and I "toss" the kids into bed, collapse on the couch, and relish the sudden quiet. But most evenings the kids and I enjoy snuggling up with books, foot and back rubs, bedtime giggles, singing and praying. My one-on-one moments at bedtime with the children often grant me an entrance into the deep waters of their hearts. They ask questions about my childhood, Jesus, heaven, friendships, and what they want to be when they are older. Some nights we tell stories about when Steve and I were kids, while other nights are for made-up stories and knock-knock jokes.

As Jesus continues to mold Steve and me, we see Him tenderly shaping the hearts and souls of our littles—though soon I will need to call them my bigs! Hallelujah! Luke, our oldest, was five years old at the start of my cancer journey. Ellie was turning four, Gracie was almost two, and Sammy J was just four months old. Now Luke is ten, Ellie is eight, Gracie is six, and Sammy J is five!

Parenting young children is physically tiring in the best of times. Parenting young children while struggling yourself with health problems is hard. *Really* hard. We are equipped only when we are immersed in the light of Jesus, His Word, and His fierce, enduring love.

The Bible is our go-to parenting book. Scripture lights our way when we are struggling with the complexities that cancer has brought. Through God's Word we gain wisdom for what news and progress we should share with the children and what we should hold back (see James 1:5). While God's Word has not erased the heartaches in our more intense moments, it has given us the light and comfort we have been so desperate for in our valley seasons.

Stay in Today

I was driving home from the grocery store one day and turned on the radio to our local station. The first words I heard were about a seventeen-year-old boy challenging everyone to go home and tell their moms that they love them. His mom had just gone home to be with the Lord.

My mind spiraled into the future, imagining Luke experiencing the same thing. Tears splashed onto the steering wheel. My momma heart wants to spare my children of all pain, despite knowing it is often pain that allows us the most intimate connection to our Savior. I fought against my churning thoughts, praying earnestly over and over, "Spirit, control my mind. Spirit, control my mind."

The Spirit brought grounding Scripture to my anxious mind: "Finally brothers and sisters, whatever is true, whatever is noble, whatever is right, whatever is pure, whatever is lovely, whatever is admirable—if anything is excellent or praiseworthy—think about such things" (Phil. 4:8, NIV).

Waves of peace swept over my soul as I inched back to the reality of today. I began the journey down gratefulness road while finishing the two-mile drive home. I spoke out the grace gifts of having the health to drive to the store, money to pay for food, a car to carry me home, a husband waiting with arms to hold me, and four beautiful children saying, "Momma! Momma!" when I entered the house.

My questions about tomorrow were not going to rob me of today's joys.

Today I celebrate miraculous growth in each of my children physically, emotionally, and spiritually. It is my joyous privilege to introduce you to each of our four children, whose little feet keep getting bigger every day! During the moments Steve and I have cried out, "Jesus, this is so hard!" Jesus has given us glimpses of bigger-picture beauty, revealing His handiwork in each of the children's hearts. Steve and I have created a faith book for each child with entries sharing how we see them growing in Jesus. We also continue to witness the power of praying God's Word over Luke, Ellie, Gracie, and Sammy J. It's a hazard to leave my bedroom in the early morning without having started the parenting journey for the day on my knees.

Meet My Medical Director

Oh, how we pray for Luke, Ellie, Gracie, and Sammy J to seek God with their whole hearts. May they love Jesus with all their hearts, minds, souls, and strength (see Mark 12:30). We pray that God would cause them to fear Him, for that is "the beginning of wisdom" (Prov. 9:10). We pray that they would be able to discern what is best and will be "pure and blameless for the day of Christ" (Phil. 1:10). We pray that as they seek to lose their lives for Jesus, they will find them. Oh, that they would fall completely in love with our beautiful Savior.

Luke Daniel, "Bringer of Light"

I take a deep breath as I write this. Luke. Just his name brings emotion from every cell in my body. From the moment Luke's newborn eyes connected with mine, there has been an intense bond between the two of us emotionally and spiritually.

Luke was five going on fifteen when I was diagnosed with cancer. His name means "bringer of light." His middle name, Daniel—he was named after my dad—means "worshiper of God." The life verse we prayed over him from the time I was pregnant with him was Luke 1:37: "Nothing is impossible with God" (NLT). That's Luke, always determined to find a way to do anything he sets his mind to, from creating music to editing videos to putting together Lego sets. He often reminds me in my moments of uncertainty that nothing is impossible with God.

From a very young age, he has had an acute awareness of good and evil, of God's power over the enemy. Even as a two-year-old, he imitated Jesus, yelling out to a storm, "Peace, be still!" It was on a spring day, when I had my oldest two children at the park. Luke was running around, while his baby sister, Ellie, was nestled against me in the Ergobaby carrier. As is typical in the Northwest, rain snuck up on us and let loose over

150

our unprotected heads. Luke stuck out his chubby little arms as far as he could. At the top of his lungs, he shouted, "Peace! Be still!"

Earlier that week Luke had heard the true story of Jesus saying this, found in Mark 4:35–41. The disciples were in a boat at sea when a great windstorm came upon them. Waves beat relentlessly against the boat, and it began to fill with water. Jesus was asleep in the boat. The disciples woke Him up, crying out, "Don't You care that we are about to sink?" Jesus immediately calmed the storm with "Peace! Be still!"

When the waters have risen around my family, I think about that stormy park day. I remember how my son trusted that Jesus could calm the wind and the waves anytime. How thankful I am that Jesus is not asleep in our storms! One word from the Savior silences the storm (see Ps. 107:29).

Luke gave his heart to Jesus on August 12, 2012. Each August 12 we celebrate his "Jesus birthday."

Luke is the child that "got it" from the first day of cancer. He has been overly aware of every pain, every test, and every possibility. He has grieved the days of sad news and celebrated the days of good news. He has frequently traveled with Steve and me to various treatment locations, including Mexico. What a joy to witness God using a young child as a vehicle of His light and love to other cancer patients and caregivers!

Luke has a heightened awareness to the emotions of others, especially my emotions. Because he is quick to notice when I am struggling physically or emotionally, sometimes I try hard to hide my feelings, but rarely do I succeed.

Through walking this road together, Jesus has increased Luke's capacity to talk about what pain feels like. After my toe surgery during the fall of 2016, I was having bone pain, and I couldn't walk. He came over to me and asked, "Momma, what is the pain like—what kind of pain do you feel?" Such tender compassion coming from an eight-year-old. God has used painful circumstances to shape His warrior, Luke, for kingdom work.

God has used my eldest son to speak truth. One night I was being antagonized by itchy bumps caused by a skin condition spreading over my body. Luke saw the frustration welling up inside me. He took me by the hand into our school room. "Remember, Momma? Remember that Jesus can heal anything?" He read to me a quote by Ann Voskamp that we had put up on the wall: "Jesus is the doctor of the body and there is no disease he cannot heal. No brokenness he cannot mend. No trouble he cannot carry. Jesus is our soul salve. The balm of Gilead. The wounded healer who touches our wounds with his and absorbs all our hurt into his healing heart."[1]

The Lord planted in Luke a love for Scripture very early on in his life. On the Sundays when I couldn't make it to church, Luke would prepare a "sermon" for us at home. I giggle as I write this, remembering how he would stand on the couch to preach with his huge Bible teetering in his little hands! He would plan everything from the music to the sermon and even to the kids' classes going on in the other room with "Teacher Ellie."

Luke loves any reason for a celebration. He is our dedicated decorator for birthdays and holidays. He loves music and spends hours worshiping by playing drums and being Mr. DJ on our synthesizer. For a few months he hosted Engelman Family Radio on the Internet. I loved sneaking up on Luke and Ellie acting out Bible stories for the radio show. My favorites were their made-up jokes and weather reports!

This boy loves to travel. We joke that while family vacations have been rare for us, cancer treatment trips have more than made up for the lack! His favorite experiences have been going to Mexico. He has kept "Luke's Log" in which he has written and drawn pictures about each trip we have taken. Luke's journaling of God's faithfulness will be something he can return to throughout his life.

One winter night when I was snuggled next to Luke, he said, "Momma, I think I want to be a pastor when I grow up. Tomorrow would you and Daddy listen to a new sermon I wrote? It has connections, Momma. You know, lots of places I can take you to in the Bible that teach about the same story. It all connects! It's about King Solomon, Momma."

I quietly rejoiced as I declared that I'd love to hear it. I glanced up to Jesus, whispering, "Thank You, Lord. Keep his love for Scripture growing, Lord. Let him hunger for more of You—always."

That same night Luke asked me to share about the book I was currently reading. *If I Perish* by Esther Ahn Kim is the book about the prisoner I mentioned in chapter 8 who was fed rotten food and survived. She shares her story of Christian persecution of the Koreans during World War II. I told Luke that this book was inspiring me to say no to self and yes to Jesus. While today we know little of intense Christian persecution here in North America, one day that may change. I told Luke how Esther had prepared for suffering by memorizing one hundred chapters of the Bible. She loved Jesus so much that she wanted to die for Him. We talked about how thinking of the home in heaven we have helps us live for Jesus better. When our words slowed down, he snuggled closer and said, "Momma, I love you. Momma, I think in the morning that I am going to study heaven in the Bible and find connections and write on that."

I left his room that night with a full heart. God has been and will continue to watch over Luke. Luke's anchor is Jesus, who is our hope that will never disappoint. As a child of God, the best is always, always yet to come.

Ellianna Joy, "The Lord Is My God"

Ellie Joy is my sensitive soul. When I was pregnant with her, Steve and I searched for a name that meant "the Lord is my God," and we settled upon Ellianna. Twenty-two-month-old Luke was so proud of his "baby didter." The way he said "Baby Ellie" came out "Bellie," which was quickly shortened to Belle. Our oldest girl still goes by Ellie or Belle in our home. Ellie struggled with frequent sickness, sensory, and anxiety issues throughout the first few years of her life. When she gave her heart to Jesus at the tender age of five on June 26, 2015, seeds of peace were sown in her that continue to bloom today.

Her life verse, which we pray over her, is Psalm 16:11: "You make known to me the path of life; in your presence there is fullness of joy; at your right hand are pleasures forevermore."

Ellie asks lots of questions—lots and lots of questions! She is an information analyst and tends to record details. We joke that we should never tell Ellie something we want to be forgotten! She will let me know if I wear the same outfit to church two Sundays in a row. We lovingly labeled her the director of our "neighborhood watch" program in our previous home. Her bedroom window faced the street. Gracie and Ellie would stand at the window, watching every person, dog, and car that passed. Ellie would give us the play by play at breakfast.

Her factual way of stating things is endearing. After my second port, a small medical device put under the skin, was placed before heading to Mexico, she randomly blurted, "Daddys don't have ports, just mommas!" Part of me wanted to cry over the fact that her momma needed a port, but giggles won!

A couple Decembers ago my sister and her husband were over for dinner, and we were discussing Christmas traditions from our childhoods. When my brother-in-law mentioned that he used to go to his grandma's house each year until she died, Ellie asked what happened to her. Upon hearing that she had died from cancer, Ellie sat quietly for a moment. Then she declared, "Momma, I am glad you are here with me. I am glad that you have not died from cancer."

My cancer diagnosis opened Ellie's eyes to heaven. She loves Jesus. She loves heaven. She dreams about what we will do there. She draws pictures of what she imagines it will be like. She declares how happy she will be when she can hug Jesus and sit in His lap.

I have seen the gift of faith at work in her young life. She seems very tuned in to God's presence, and perhaps this is what fuels all her questions! She walked into her class at church on Pentecost Sunday this year excited to celebrate the special day. When I picked her up, she declared, "Momma, I don't think anyone in my class knew what today was!" I explained to her that it was only because of an e-mail from a sweet sister in Christ that we had been inspired to celebrate Pentecost Sunday this year for the first time! We prayed for God to awaken us to the reality of His presence in us. I tremble imagining what it must have been like for the people present on the Day of Pentecost. We have that same power at work in us today—such a gift!

Because of her struggles with eczema, Ellie needs to avoid certain food items that cause flare-ups. She emphatically declares that when she gets to heaven, she will get to eat whatever she wants, because there is no eczema in heaven. She asks if I would please not go ahead to heaven and instead wait until we can all go together as a family of six.

She finally lost her first tooth—months after her little sister did, much to her chagrin! Ellie has recently started the piano lessons she has dreamed of for months! It is a joy to watch her avidly soak it in and join Luke in worship time. The other day I saw on her desk the first to-do list I have seen her make. She had put on the list "devotions, listen to Christian music, read the Bible to Gracie, get dressed, clean room." God is working in her to will and to act according to His good purpose (see Phil. 2:13)! I will hold fast to this during the hard moments of parenting.

Here are some of my cherished Ellie quotes:

155

- "I wish I could find heaven on our globe."
- "I can feel my heart beeping."
- "I love God and Jesus and Lord."
- "I hope I can take Diddy to heaven when I go so Jesus can fix her." (Diddy is her lovey bunny that she has had since birth. It's tattered beyond recognition. After several Diddy surgeries with duct tape, sewing, and iron-on patches, Ellie was recently informed that Diddy is no longer fixable by any earthly means!)
- "Luke, I want to marry you." (She has since realized that she cannot marry her big brother and has declared instead that she will marry my friend's little boy and have six children—and all of them are named.)

I think back on that Christmas day right after diagnosis, and Ellie had just turned four years old a week prior. She is now eight years old. The most recent gift from Jesus has been her freedom from a severe fear of dogs! Instead of running away from dogs with blood-curdling screams, she now runs looking for dogs when we go to play at parks. She is blossoming under the tender care of Jesus like a delicate yet beautiful desert flower. *Thank You, Jesus!*

Gracelyn Elizabeth, "Loving-Kindness, Favor"

Gracie girl was born at one ounce under eleven pounds! It was a rough beginning that included me landing back in the hospital for triple infections shortly after her birth. Thankfully the hospital staff allowed five-day-old Gracie to stay with me.

She and I spent her first Christmas Eve alone together in the hospital room. Steve had gone home to be with Luke and Ellie overnight. I was hooked up to IVs with her eleven-pound, bobbly newborn self nestled against me. I alternated between tears of frustration and moments of contentment. I watched the clock hit two in the morning while singing Christmas songs to her, watching the rhythmic drip of antibiotics entering my body. Between the pain from the C-section and the infections as well as the position of the needles in my arms, we resembled a circus when it came time to nurse Gracie. I spent the time in between feedings planning my next nursing strategy. Every movement hurt, but feeding Gracie was worth it.

I counted down the minutes to when Luke and Ellie would be awake and Steve could return with them. We all spent a memorable Christmas morning together in the hospital. I was grateful to be together as a family.

Gracie has been a tangible reminder of God's grace to me with her easygoing nature, generous heart, and thankfulness for little things. She has gone from being a happy baby to a happy toddler to a happy young girl. The life verse we chose for Gracie is 2 Corinthians 9:8: "God is able to make all grace abound to you, so that having all sufficiency in all things at all times, you may abound in every good work."

Very early on in her life, Gracie began to ask questions about Jesus. Pure joy courses through me when my children ask about heaven and Jesus! Homeschooling gifts us a slow start to our day. We have time to watch birds, squirrels, lizards, and clouds. Sometimes we choose to do our Bible and school time together in the backyard, relishing the warm sunshine and feeling the grass under our feet.

Gracie loves to read, do school, and draw. She has declared that she wants to be an artist when she grows up. I love watching her teach Sammy J his "school" and spend hours in pretend play.

Gracie was created to love big. Her happiness splashes over onto everyone around her. I love to squeeze her tight and bury my face in her sweetness.

Lest I forget to share about Gracie's difficulties, I must reveal that she has been caught sneaking art supplies! She took an entire roll of plastic wrap from the kitchen drawer to wrap gifts for us. One year for Christmas we found more than forty gifts buried under the low-hanging branches at the back of our Christmas tree. Apparently she had been wrapping her belongings from her room in white paper to hide under the tree. We've decided that she will need to open her own tree farm to keep up her paper supply, because now she is on rations!

On October 22, 2016, she tugged on my arm and whispered, "Momma, I want to give Jesus my heart." At first I questioned if she really understood, at the age of four, what that meant. We asked her questions, and we agreed that she was ready! We knelt by her bed together for her to pray.

We are grateful to Jesus for continuing to show Himself to Gracie, drawing her into Himself. One morning I asked her not to climb up on the rail over the backyard deck. She asked what would happen if she fell off. I told her that she would be hurt very badly and that it would be very possible that she could never walk again. She declared, "If I can't walk, Momma, I will have to sit on the couch all day, all the time, until, until—Jesus comes back!"

May her young eyes always have the return of our Savior on her radar.

Samuel Jeremiah, "Heard by God"

Sweet Sammy J was a four-month-old sleeping baby in the ER room with Steve and me when the doctors walked in to announce cancer. In disbelief I looked at his chubby cheeks, unable to process what I had just heard. I wanted to blink my eyes and wake up at home, tucked safely into bed next to Steve. I wanted to get up from my own bed and peek in on the children all sound asleep in their own beds.

Devastation and fear set in when I was whisked up to a different floor of the hospital and Steve took Sammy J home until seven the next morning, when visiting hours would start. As my milk for Sammy started coming in soon after they left, I thought it strange that my body was still working even though my world had crashed. Questions attacked me as I counted the minutes until Sammy would warm my arms again.

In the days that followed at the hospital, Sammy was a gift from God to me. Holding and feeding him reminded me to keep breathing as we awaited news from test after test. I look back and see how God has watched over Sammy J from the very start.

His name has a story. As a four-year-old, Luke prayed daily for a baby boy to be in my tummy. When we found out we were pregnant, with Gracie only ten months old, we knew this must be the baby boy Luke had prayed for! We chose the name Samuel, because it means "heard by God." We chose Jeremiah because we love the meaning of it: "the Lord will raise up." We had no idea when we prayed over the name Jeremiah how much I would need the reminder that God is raising up this boy!

They say it takes a village to raise a family. This has been especially true for this baby boy. I am eternally grateful for my family and friends who have helped Steve and me nurture this baby boy into toddlerhood and now into a rambunctious, fun-loving boy. Sammy J's life verse is 1 Samuel 12:24: "Only fear the LORD and serve him faithfully with all your heart. For consider what great things he has done for you."

Sammy is a unique combination of "all boy" and snuggler. Sammy J loves to have "fwiends." He loves to run and give hugs. He often comes up to us and rubs our shoulders. He will whisper, "Momma, you're beautiful." He begs me to snuggle with him at every nap and bedtime. After finishing his dinner he rushes over to sit on my lap while Daddy reads from the Bible.

Our bedroom door squeaks open in the early morning hours as Sammy's little feet tiptoe to our bed. I love the early morning snuggle time when I can enjoy Sammy's stillness. It seems that from the moment Sammy is vertical, he is moving until bedtime. Steve's theory on the energy of little children is that they are stealing it from all the adults around them. One of my favorite things about Sammy is watching him dance.

When Sammy J was three years old, he and I went for a walk together in early February around the neighborhood. He remembered the first flowers of spring from the previous year. He pointed out the daffodils getting ready to bloom, excited for warmer weather and more park days. I had him look up at the blustery trees and huge clouds moving quickly across the sky. I said, "Sammy J, one day Jesus is coming back for us. Those clouds will move away, and there He will be."

Sammy said, "Where, Momma? I don't see Him!"

"Soon, Sammy J, soon."

One day winter will be past, and spring will come—and spring will stay.

Spending Our Moments

"Time is a treasure, and once lost is never to be found again."[2] In his story *The Bird's Nest*, Christoph Von Schmid tells of a special relationship between a young prince, his tutor, and a shepherd boy. The tutor observed the wise shepherd boy hungrily reading books while caring for the sheep. Wanting to encourage his pupil to be on guard against the wasting of time, he shares from Scripture the story of the boy who gave his lunch to Jesus.

Jesus took one little boy's lunch and fed thousands of people with it. Next Jesus told the disciples to "gather up the leftover fragments, that nothing will be lost." The leftovers filled *twelve* baskets (see John 6:13)!

How we spend our moments matters. When parenting young children, seeking God early in the morning is what works best for me. During the day Jesus gives me additional fragments of time.

Our days can easily fill up with tasks that occupy our hands. Worries keep our minds running on a treadmill. Jesus empowers us to recapture these fragments of time. We can turn them into cherished minutes to sneak in another bite of His Word, thank Him for a blessing, pray for a hurting friend, connect with a child's heart, speak a word of encouragement, or enjoy the music of nature. We can mentally release to Jesus the concerns that have crept their way into our hearts during the day. We can fall back into the arms of Jesus and rest a moment, cradled in His strong arms.

Considering the cross is a heart-changing way to spend five free minutes in our days. At the end of a day we will be amazed at what Jesus taught us within those fragments of time. Maybe our children will learn something new about Jesus and our eternal home. Maybe a blessing will not slip by unnoticed. Our souls will become a bit fatter, our minds will be renewed, and our bodies will be refreshed by His living water.

Sharpening Arrows

The enemy loves to strike in our most vulnerable spots. My kids are mine. I want to raise them. I want to teach them everything God continues to teach me. I want to be the one to help them through their teenage years, college, marriage, and parenting. I want to be called Grandma.

But more than that, I want my children to be arrows for the kingdom, sharpened by God's Word, ready to live and die for their King. I yearn for the eyes of their souls to have a clear view of eternity's shore, giving purpose to their days. God gets to decide what He uses to shape my kids. I choose to trust. Each day

I practice visually lifting my kids up to Him and releasing them. They are not mine; they are His. He loves them fiercely. Every promise in Scripture that is true for me is true for them. He will not leave them or forsake them.

Recently I was reading through Isaiah and came across a beautiful passage of Scripture speaking to the way God teaches us each uniquely:

> Give ear, and hear my voice; give attention, and hear my speech. Does he who plows for sowing plow continually? Does he continually open and harrow his ground? When he has leveled its surface, does he not scatter dill, sow cumin, and put in wheat in rows and barley in its proper place, and emmer as the border? For he is rightly instructed; his God teaches him.
>
> Dill is not threshed with a threshing sledge, nor is a cart wheel rolled over cumin, but dill is beaten out with a stick, and cumin with a rod. Does one crush grain for bread? No, he does not thresh it forever, when he drives his cart wheel over it with his horses, he does not crush it. This also comes from the LORD of hosts; he is wonderful in counsel and excellent in wisdom. (Isa. 28:23–29)

In the same way that God knows best what tools to use to shape our souls for Himself, He will equip us as parents to nurture each of our children's hearts. Regardless of what circumstances we face, the Lord of hosts, the Lord of angel armies fights ahead of us, behind us, and beside us. Excellent in wisdom, wonderful in counsel—this is our God.

Abba, as many days as You give me breath, let me be the living expression of Your loving kindness to my children. Let it radiate from my eyes, be felt in my touch, be seen in my smile, and be heard in my words. Please grant to Luke, Ellie, Gracie, and Sammy J wholehearted devotion that they may keep Your commandments. Let them be strong and courageous, not afraid or dismayed, for You, Lord, our God, are with them. Speak often to them Your promise that You will not leave them or forsake them. They are Yours, Lord. Thank You for the years You are giving me to sharpen these arrows for Your kingdom. My heart is so very, very full. Amen.

Kinetic Love

We were created to orbit around our triune God. God the Father, Jesus His only begotten Son, and the Holy Spirit have enjoyed self-existing, perfect fellowship that has had no beginning and knows no end. Our uncreated triune God is love defined, an enduring, unshakable, and unbreakable love. His Spirit is our life breath, upholding our lives with each beat of our hearts. This is our God. Hallelujah!

God's love is the force that spoke everything into existence, including us. God's love is kinetic, in constant motion. It pulls us toward Himself, and with it He fills us up before sending us out to be His love to others. His love grounds us in the same way gravity holds our feet on planet Earth. When we travel around Jesus as our center, all is right in our world. When we inch Him off the throne of our hearts, we lose our power, our peace, our hope, and our capacity to truly love.

We Are Greatly Loved

The winter of 2016 was exceptionally cold and snowy in the Northwest. With the onset of the cold winter came a steeper slope for our family. My husband was slammed with antagonistic and widespread eczema. Steve's systemic bleeding and blistering eluded true help from any physician we sought care from. We went through every natural remedy we were given from Dr. Google, friends, and family. Yet eczema remained. The daily physical battle became spiritually heightened in the nighttime hours when Steve's eczema was roaring—bleeding, blistering, itching, and spreading.

Alongside Steve's eczema came the crash of my adrenal glands. Soon afterward I began having monthly migraines. All this along with my limping immune system raised the question, "What do I do now? My caregiver needs caregiving. Our kids need help."

I cried. I cried hard. Especially at nights when Steve stayed downstairs warring against eczema and the havoc it brought. In the midst of my intense sobs one night when I was feeling alone, a voice from the Lord reminded me from within that "I am my beloved's, and his desire is for me" (Song of Sol. 7:10).

We are intensely loved. In his book *The Furious Longing of God*, Brennan Manning describes the intensity of this love that our Beloved has for us:

> The foundation of the furious longing of God is the Father who is the originating Lover, the Son who is the full SELF expression of that love, and the Spirit, who is the original and inexhaustible activity of that Love, drawing the created universe into itself.[1]

The truth in Song of Solomon that God's desire is for us carries comfort. God loves us. He is furiously in love with us. God was not whacking my family with a stick to see just how much suffering we could endure. His desire is for me—to make me more like Him, to be to me the One I treasure most and look to first, even before my sweet husband. When I seek Jesus as my First Love, I am better equipped to love horizontally.

When Jesus is our greatest treasure, we become more sensitive to the presence of sin in our lives. Unconfessed habitual sin will harm all horizontal relationships. Two frequent invaders that come my way when I do not feel well are a sense of entitlement and self-pity. Thoughts invade: *What am I supposed to do now that Steve is being hit too? Who is going to take care of the kids? What about me?* The world around me gets smaller as I get bigger.

Frequently, in the painful moments, when I want desperately to hang on to my hurt, Jesus uses Scripture to release me from the greater pain of wanting anything more than Him. Steve's eczema season took me to Proverbs 31. Jesus stirred a desire in me for the heart of my husband to trust me during his valley, that he would have no lack of gain. I wanted to bring him good and not harm all the days of my life (see Prov. 31:11–12).

Speaking encouragement and bringing Steve good when he hurt found its root in my acknowledging the truth that Jesus is my Beloved and that His desire is for me. Loving another in this way is overflow, not work. When we sit at the feet of our Beloved, coming into awareness of our union with Him, we find that He is our faucet and offers a limitless flow of love, joy, peace, patience, kindness, goodness, gentleness, and self-control. From Him we receive constant, complete filling, bearing the fruit of His Spirit, which inevitably spills over to everyone around us. It becomes quickly obvious when I have disconnected from my supply of living water—my fruit bearing ceases, my soul becomes parched, and my heart gets tired.

During Steve's season of debilitation, I found an increased need to dress myself each morning with God's strength (see Prov. 31:17). Clothing myself with the Lord Jesus Christ is my only hope of being strong when I am weak (see Rom. 13:14; 2 Cor. 12:10).

Two questions became frequent flyers in my war room each morning:

1. Is the teaching of kindness on my tongue? "She opens her mouth with wisdom, and the teaching of kindness is on her tongue" (Prov. 31:26).
2. Am I seeking first God's kingdom above all, even above my husband (see Matt. 6:33)? God's kingdom is about selfless love, not selfish love. Instead of asking, "How can my husband meet my needs?" I want to be looking to meet his needs through the power of the Holy Spirit in me.

Not long ago our family stood on a pier, staring into the dark, swirling ocean below. I watched my children leaning slightly over the rails to get a better look. Looking down into the water made us all want to be careful not to lean too far over that railing! Beyond those waters a gorgeous sunset was in the making. Orange, pink, and purple light shot out across the waves. The contrast between the scary ocean waters and the glorious sunset reminded me of the ending of *Little Pilgrim's Progress*, when Christiana is invited to cross the dark river and enter the Celestial City. "Sometimes she stole away quietly with Mercy to walk by the side of the Dark River. The sight of the troubled waters made Mercy tremble, but Christiana always looked beyond them at the beautiful golden light."[2]

Will we look beyond any waters troubling our souls, our husband's or wife's, our children's, our family's, to the beautiful light of Jesus beyond?

Love Serves

Love keeps no record of wrong (see 1 Cor. 13:5). Keeping track of others' wrongs stops love in its tracks.

People's wrongs creep into our subconscious and set up home in our hearts. Grudges, unforgiveness, and bitterness become debilitating bricks in backpacks meant to be abandoned at the foot of the cross. Jesus empowers us to travel lightly so we can do everything in love (see 1 Cor. 16:14). The ways of our Lord are not of this world. God asks us not to repay evil for evil but always to seek to do good to everyone (see 1 Thess. 5:15–18).

Becoming a student of the people around us equips us to love them in the ways they feel it best. For some love is time. For others love is service. But for all love is something we experience. God is love. He sent His only Son, Jesus, as the tangible expression of His perfect love. Reading the life of Jesus Christ in the four Gospels shows us that to love is to serve.

When Jesus ascended into heaven after His resurrection, love didn't disappear with Him. The Holy Spirit came to remind us of everything Jesus had taught us, including how to love. Through Christ's Holy Spirit, our hearts are flooded by His love. This protects us from futile attempts to love when our tanks are on empty. The Holy Spirit directs each yes and no to protect us from overloaded schedules that reduce our capacity for extending kinetic love.

To love God is to obey Him. To obey Him is to love others as He loves them. If loving others feels like a burden, it's time for us to return to our First Love for renewal of heart, body, mind, and soul. For His commands are not burdensome (see 1 John 5:2–3).

Margin for Honor

One practice that helps in loving people with God's love is leaving a margin for honor in our days so we have time to love someone when the need arises. We leave margins on a page. We leave margins for error. Jesus tells a story about another margin in Luke 10:25–37—a margin for honor.

A Jewish man on a trip was robbed and beaten, left to bleed to death on the side of a road. A priest came by. Surely this man of God would help this broken one. He passed by. Then a Levite approached. Levites were men chosen to work in the temple—another high-probability rescue agent. But he too passed by. As the third man came along, the injured man looked up but quickly averted his eyes in utter defeat. This stranger heading toward him was a Samaritan. Samaritans despised Jews.

Then it happened. The footsteps slowed to a stop. The dust settled around those enemy feet. The eyes of the broken looked up. Hurt met Healer. The universal language of love did all the talking. This kind of love quiets the thoughts of abandonment. "A Samaritan, as he traveled, came where the man was; and when he saw him, he took pity on him" (Luke 10:33, NIV).

This Samaritan pulled out his oil and wine, sparing no expense. He cleaned. He bandaged. He gently transported the injured man to a safe haven to recover. He even guaranteed reimbursement to the innkeeper for the entire recovery. All for a stranger.

Jesus told this story about honor in response to a question by an expert in Jewish law. This teacher wanted to know exactly who his neighbors were that he was to love in order to gain eternal life. Can't you just see this list on his clipboard that he wanted to use to check-box his way into heaven? His path was marked by effort, exhaustion, a personal agenda, and the freedom to pass by anyone or anything seen as an interruption.

Jesus said gently, "Sit down; I have a story to tell you. 'Love your neighbor' means love as I love. You are broken in the road, with an empty wallet, deserving of nothing. I am your good Samaritan, with everything to give, freely offering. As you receive to overflowing, let it brim over to others."

Honor is about maximum love, not minimum. Honor requires leaving time in our days for the unexpected. It flows from a heart full of grace. This grace is present because of Jesus' costly grace—grace that equips, grace that strengthens, grace that comes from our Savior who will never pass us by.

In Acts 20:35 we read that it is more blessed to give than to receive. Jesus created us to experience happiness when we give to others. He empowers us to move from "I hope things get better for you" to "How can I help?"

Mankind desires to be loved. We look to people only to find human love insufficient for the soul. Jesus is true love. Jesus transforms our stagnant love into His vibrant love. We are His vessels as we give to others the love that He so freely gives to us.

I join Amy Carmichael's prayer to be clear air through which the love of God passes unhindered to thirsty souls:

Love through me, Love of God,
Make me like Thy clear air
Through which unhindered, colours pass
As though it were not there.

Powers of the love of God,
Depths of the heart Divine,
O Love that faileth not, break forth,
And flood this world of Thine.[3]

Lord, You did not pass me by. You saw me at the cross, and You see me now, my ever-present good Samaritan. Let me "go and do likewise." Jesus, may Your all-powerful unfailing love break forth and flood this world! Amen.

In My Medicine Cabinet

Several times during my first years of cancer treatment I experienced a sudden urge to toss every supplement in my home into the trash. Instead, the supplements we didn't end up sticking with were shoved into the office. It became downright dangerous to open the cupboard where our supplements were stuffed. I wanted to throw a blanket over my head and hide when faced with new patient paperwork, since most forms gave ten lines for medications but a measly three for "herbs, vitamins, and other supplements."

Fear purchased those first supplements. A turning point came a few months after diagnosis, when buying the next supplement became financially crippling. We recognized the pattern of turning to the next herb as the answer to our need. Google is helpful but not always trustworthy. Only Jesus is worthy of our total trust as our guide. He delights in every detail of our lives (see Ps. 37:23).

Jesus, my Medical Director, has led Steve and me during our five-year journey. My pattern for receiving new information remains the same today: I can only take in a small dose of information at a time before needing to sit with Jesus and talk to Him about it. In His time, and it's always His time, He gives me peace. His peace is my green light to proceed. A yellow light means caution. Moving too quickly on a yellow light has led to regret. Proceeding during a red light is hazardous. Sometimes I test the waters, but I am prepared to pull back if something new we are trying is affecting me adversely.

The peace Jesus gives is not a guarantee that I will never see cancer again this side of heaven. It's a stillness of soul, a peace that I am being obedient to the path He has called me to. I can walk confidently in the One who sits enthroned over every circumstance. He reminds me that I am not a statistic; I am His precious daughter. He absolutely will see my life through to its intended completion. This truth sets me free from the shackles of fear.

Figuring Out Alternative Treatments

When I was diagnosed at Christmas of 2013, I didn't know anyone who'd had cancer who had not pursued conventional medicine. Our hope was to avoid conventional medicine, but we felt alone and intimidated by the myriad of options on the less-traveled path of alternative medicine. The Internet was at times helpful and other times a web of confusion. Without prayer I was trapped like a helpless fly in a web of despair.

In choosing the first treatments, we had our little ones to consider. All the places that offered non-toxic cancer treatments required traveling for us. Many were not covered by insurance. We chose to stay home initially and start down the list of inexpensive natural protocols. We started using essential oils. We also followed the Budwig protocol and then transitioned to Gerson therapy. Each effort taught us something we could adopt into an anti-cancer lifestyle. We found that we did better using what worked for our family and letting go of the rest. Protocols can become prison cells if not under the leading of the Spirit.

I created a "top twenty-five" list of home-based healthcare strategies in response to numerous e-mails from people asking for help. I share that list in this chapter. I am not a cancer expert by any means; I am just a girl—a girl with one stellar husband and four delightful children to raise up while feeling the best I possibly can, a girl who loves Jesus and desires not to bring harm to my body. My body is the temple of the living God. He is my breath. My heart beats in this moment because of His upholding. My list is simply a record of what has been helpful for us.

While my top *non*-home-based recommendations would be Hope4Cancer and PIOH, the list below provides home-based terrain changers—things that make the body less friendly to those cancer cells.

These twenty-five cancer weapons are our favorites from the last five years, but certainly you will meet other people who have completely different lists. Ask Jesus, and He will help you. "If any of you lacks wisdom, let him ask God, who gives generously to all without reproach, and it will be given him" (James 1:5).

Dear readers, fear has been an unwanted intruder in my heart numerous times. Fear still comes knocking. Don't answer the door to fear! Fear is a liar. Fear is a thief. The only cure for my fear has been sweet Jesus. I pray for each cancer patient or caregiver reading through this list to be protected from the evil three: fear, doubt, and discouragement. I despise them! These flaming arrows from the evil one have no place in our hearts and our homes.

Our shield of faith is able to protect us. I like to imagine Jesus in front of me, shielding me from the enemy's arrows. My faith is not in how strong I am but in how big *He* is. My faith is in His presence and power over all things.

I pray that you will meet Jesus on these pages. May His peace flood your soul. We were not created to carry the burden of curing ourselves. Jesus is our burden bearer, our great Physician. He will fight for us and bring us home when our purpose here on Earth is complete. In that moment our eyes will lock with our Savior's compassionate gaze, love radiating. All else will fade. In that moment, whether we are ninety-six, like my grandpa was, or younger, we will know victory in every way.

My Top Twenty-Five Home-Based Cancer Weapons

1. *Prayer*. Above anything, prayer is my number one. Always. Sometimes I forget to breathe. Anxiety can make you do that. But Jesus is my peace and directs my paths. He is my great Reward. He reminds me to breathe, and to breathe deeply. Deep breathing gets oxygen to where it needs to go. I pray with my hands over where cancer has been and ask Jesus to grant His divine healing, to bring order where there is chaos in my cells. I pray with my face to the floor, on walks, and outside while staring up at the clouds. I love to lie on my bedroom floor on my back with my arms out in the cross position. I think of Jesus on the cross, and I thank Him for His death and resurrection. After I pray and surrender all to Him, I stay a moment longer to wiggle my fingers and toes, releasing anything I am holding onto except my Savior.

2. *Clean diet.* While in Mexico for cancer treatment, my oncologist taught me to rotate my diet about every three months. Diversity keeps cancer cells guessing and delights the palate as well. Low-starch veggies remain a part of my daily consumption, while other things rotate in and out. I like to describe my diet as the Spirit-led diet. It involves Jesus helping me through decisions of what is right for each day given my current circumstances.

We eat in season, local, and organic as often as possible. We love sprouted nuts and seeds. By making our own nut and seed butters, we can choose sprouted nuts and seeds, safe oils, and healthy salt. I grind up pumpkin seeds and flax seeds the first half of my menstrual cycle and then switch to grinding up sesame seeds and sunflower seeds for the second half to help balance hormones. We cook with ghee, coconut oil, and avocado oil. We love olive oil on salads and use red palm oil on squash or wild rice. We rotate in wild-caught fish and lentils. We sometimes use spaghetti squash as "noodles" and cauliflower "rice" for less starchy meal options. Root vegetables make the best chips. Roasted sweet potatoes and carrot fries are family favorites! Squashes are nourishing to the spleen, and they color our plates several times a week. Delicata squash is delicious!

We try to have bone broth three to four days a week. Smoothies are another regular item. I use pea protein, chard, almond milk, chia seeds, flax seeds, and berries to make protein smoothies. Sometimes I add acerola or camu camu powder for a vitamin C boost. I currently regularly have wild rice and make homemade granola with shredded coconut, hemp seeds, chia seeds, sunflower seeds, coconut oil, and spices. We eat a moderate amount of fruit each day, especially berries. The children love sliced apples for dessert after dinner.

How we eat is as important as *what* we eat. We drink our solids and chew our liquids. This ensures that the digestion process starts where God designed it to begin: in the mouth. Even when drinking smoothies, "chewing" it first allows it to mix with saliva to be digested effectively. Mealtimes are a time for slowing down, savoring bites of food, sharing stories from our day. Kids say the funniest things, especially at mealtimes! We are still working on manners and not getting up and down throughout the meal, but it's getting better all the time as the children grow. Steve or Luke reads from the family Bible after dinner. I love watching Steve dramatize the soul food for the children. I know they will grow up remembering Daddy reading the Bible.

3. *Juicing.* I started with carrot juice (the Hallelujah Diet) in 2014, using a Champion juicer. Then we transitioned to a morning juice with ginger root, carrots, and beets. Immunity juice has been a favorite in our home, especially with our youngest. His five-year-old feet come running the moment he hears the juicer start up. Our immunity juice is made with carrots, turmeric root, ginger root, and an orange.

Some mornings we start the day off with warm lemon water—the juice of half a lemon in about eight ounces of water. Green juices can be delicious when you throw in a bit of green apple, pear, or lemon and ginger. Our current morning juice includes lemon, ginger root, parsley, cilantro, kale, celery, beet, green apple, cucumber, and a couple of carrots. It's delicious! When I struggled with estrogen dominance symptoms, we juiced red cabbage to help metabolize the extra estrogen.

4. *Sleep.* Going to bed by ten and getting up at six provides the best sleeping hours for our immune systems. It's important not to be around phones or laptops or any blue light, which prevents melatonin production. I use cedarwood or Young Living's Peace & Calming essential-oil blend to help me sleep.

5. *Daily ten.* Take ten minutes, close your eyes, and go with Jesus to a favorite place. I love to picture being on a mountaintop, next to a creek, or walking by the ocean with Him. Spend time imagining every detail of what heaven will be like. Go watch clouds or stars, or stare out the window. Focus on being alone with Jesus, giving Him each fear you are holding onto. Imagine the day you will get to see Him face to Face. I remind myself that any suffering here increases the weight of glory there. My connection with Him in these quiet hours helps me stay aware of His presence in the chaotic hours.

6. *Coffee enemas.* These help detoxify the liver. People do this multiple times a day if they are doing the Gerson protocol. I tried that in the early part of my cancer journey but found that it was too much for me. Coffee enemas are not something all healthcare professionals promote. I can speak from my own experience, however, that I have been tremendously helped by doing coffee enemas over the last five years.

7. *Digestion.* Taking hydrochloric acid (HCL) and digestive enzymes with meals helps digest food. Also,

taking a little apple cider vinegar mixed with warm water before eating can help with proper digestion.

8. *Laughter.* Remember to laugh out loud. I realized a few months ago that I did more laughing over texting ("LOL") than laughing out loud. To laugh is to live free. Proverbs 31:25 states, "Strength and dignity are her clothing, and she laughs at the time to come."

9. *Pure water.* We drink structured water.[1] Early on we purchased a Kangen water machine to produce water with a pH of 9.5, but now we mostly use it for drinking 7.0 pH pure water away from meals. I stop drinking water an hour before I eat and wait until two hours after eating to drink again.

10. *Sauna.* The sauna we have in our garage is one of the best purchases we have made for home healthcare. I use it two to three times a week. I love to listen to sermons, pray, and sing in the sauna. Last year we also acquired the hyperthermia sauna dome. I have found that I need several days to recover in between my sessions in the "pizza oven," as my cancer clinic family calls it. It sure makes my kids giggle when I declare, "Momma's going in the pizza oven!"

11. *PEMF mat.* PEMF stands for "pulsed electromagnetic field." We learned about PEMF mats from the first integrative treatment center we visited in Irvine in January 2014. It's in my top twenty-five for being both healing and relaxing to the body. The benefits are numerous and can be read about on www.drpawluk.com.

12. *Castor oil packs.* Castor oil packs will reduce pain, increase liver function, and stimulate lymphatics. I apply my favorite essential oils to the castor oil pack. I soak wool with castor oil and place it directly on my skin; then I place plastic wrap over it and place a

heating pad on top of that. I leave it on my abdomen/ liver for thirty to sixty minutes and then shower it off. It feels good when you get past the sliminess of it.

13. *Essential oils.* I use a blend of sacred frankincense, myrrh, clove, and sage topically. I love the KidScents by Young Living for the children. My children's first reaction when they have an owie or if they are sick is wondering what oil we will use. I use oils to make homemade cleaners, toothpaste, room deodorizers, and hand soaps. We diffuse Young Living's Thieves essential-oil blend in the air to kill airborne viruses and bacteria and lighten the load on our bodies' defense systems. On our skin we use coconut, jojoba, grape-seed, emu, and almond oils mixed with essential oils. We make cleaning products with essential oils mixed into vinegar, baking soda, and castile soap. I make hand soap with one third castile soap, two thirds water, and a few drops of Thieves, and we buy hand-pump bottles from Amazon to put it in. It's simple and cost effective!

14. *Infrared heat lamp.* We found the same heat lamp I used at Hope4Cancer in Mexico on Amazon. I use this for a half hour each morning, eighteen inches away from my body over the affected areas.

15. *Essiac tea.* This is a blood cleanser and good for fighting cancer. I used it for a couple weeks and then rested from it a couple weeks for the first two years. I still use it periodically for a blood-cleaning boost.

16. *Photon therapy.* We purchased laser pads like the ones I used at Hope4Cancer. I do it a few days a week to reduce any pain and inflammation. You can read more about these at www.inlightmedical.com.

17. *Internet search.* Find a designated web searcher—someone willing to do healthcare searches for you. This

protects you from spiraling into "what ifs" and utter confusion. Taking in all that Google points us to can overwhelm our hearts, bodies, and minds.

18. *Daily double.* A brisk walk two times a day keeps the lymphatic system moving. You can do this with an elliptical, a Cellerciser (mini trampoline), or a slow jog outside in the morning with a walk later in the day. The concept is to be moving twice a day.

19. *Basic supplements.* Whenever possible, I choose a food source or other natural source rather than a supplement for specific nutritional needs. For example, I use egg yolks for B12, the sun for vitamin D, and turmeric root rather than a turmeric supplement. Turmeric is an excellent anti-inflammatory. Besides taking HCL and digestive enzymes, I rotate through a variety of other supplements. The frequent flyers include vitamin C, probiotics, Inflammation Balance from Carlson Labs (DHA), Dr. Jockers Brain Calm Magnesium, Dr. Jockers GI Regulator, Immune Power Plus from Baseline Health Products, and multi-vitamins and electrolytes from Seeking Health. If we are doing a parasite cleanse, we add on microbials and supplements to support the liver, colon, and kidneys.

20. *Hugs.* Hug at least twelve times a day. I heard a TED talk once that said to thrive we should get twelve a day. I love hugs. My favorite way to be greeted is, "It's good to see you, Lisa," with a snug-as-a-bug kind of a hug.

21. *Oil pulling.* I take a tablespoon of coconut oil with a couple drops of clove and peppermint essential oils added in. After letting it melt in my mouth, I "pull" it through my teeth back and forth, swishing it all around for about ten minutes. Then I spit it into the toilet, because it can clog the sink drains. It whitens

your teeth as it removes plaque while killing viruses and bacteria. Your immune system receives a boost! It is truly refreshing!

22. *Grounding* (also known as earthing). We learned about grounding early on, at our first treatment facility in Irvine, California. We didn't think much of it at the time, as we were suffering from information overload. Recently, through dear friends, we were introduced again to the idea that having our skin in contact with the earth's surface helps reduce the effect of living in a modern-day "positive charge" era. Our bodies are electrical and need to be grounded. Grounding our bodies trades positive electrical stress for free electrons. This occurred naturally and frequently in past cultures in which people were barefoot or had shoe soles made of organic-based materials. But the advent of the rubber sole began the decline of grounding for the general population. The best thing about grounding is that it's free! Steve and I started taking off our shoes and socks and playing with our children in the backyard. We love it when we can make the one-hour drive to the ocean to go barefoot there! We have noticed improved energy and sleep. Others who have chronic pain and inflammation have seen it go away through grounding.

23. *Natural pain medication.* We have found Arnica pellets and cream, essential oils, Curamin (a turmeric/ frankincense combo), magnesium oil or lotion, Epsom salt baths, and homemade muscle-relief creams to be quite effective in reducing moderate pain levels. The family favorites for massaging into skin are jojoba, emu, coconut, almond, and grape-seed oils. Mixing wintergreen, peppermint, PanAway (an oil blend from Young Living), and copaiba into these oils and

massaging into the skin helps Steve and me a lot. For the children, usually the lavender grape-seed blend is all they need, because it's the love of a parent they really need for their owies.

24. *Service.* If we have breath, we have something to offer someone. It may be writing a card to put in the mail the old-fashioned way. Maybe it's a smile. During one of our hospital stays, we met another lymphoma patient. Steve thought of surprising the patient's caregiver with some fresh juice and a healthy snack from a local juice bar. It was a small thing that gave a big boost to her and to us.

Numerous times we have been on the receiving end of service. Each time a stranger extends kindness to me, I am inspired to become a burden-lifter for people I cross paths with. One way I can serve in my home is to speak the truth of Scripture to Steve and the children. Another fun way to put a smile on the children's faces is to play with them—whatever they want to play. It can be a made-up game, a board game, or something outside. Sometimes we will be surprised by what we can still do, even with health struggles. Each day that comes brings new opportunities to be the love and light of Jesus to whoever enters our moments.

25. *Forgiveness.* Daily evaluate the soil of the heart. We travel light when we don't keep any record of wrongs. When I check the soil of my heart for weeds of bitterness, envy, and unforgiveness and then ask the Spirit to pluck those, I experience lightweight joy. Choosing to forgive puts a spring in our steps. Sin, on the other hand, moves dark clouds into view, bringing chains of depression and discouragement. Jesus

died to set us free from the bondage of sin and enable us to live victorious Christian lives. Colossians 3 is my favorite passage to pray through when I'm struggling emotionally or in relationships. It teaches me how to love as Jesus loves. I can think of nothing else I'd rather have in my medicine cabinet than the peace and joy Jesus gives.

New ideas are always coming to add to our list. Steve and I keep open minds as we soak in new information. We ask Jesus about it, remembering that what's most important is not what's in our medicine cabinets but what's in our hearts. Jesus tells us that "it is not what goes into the mouth that defiles a person, but what comes *out* of the mouth; this defiles a person" (Matt. 15:11). It is out of the overflow of our hearts that our mouths speak (see Matt. 12:34). I can spend energy trying to eat clean food and take high-quality supplements, but if that becomes more important than Jesus, idolatry takes hold of my heart.

Jesus, My North Star

Smartphones have rescued me from a terrible sense of direction. As a child, I went to the same location six days a week for school and church, about ten minutes from home. Yet my dad joked to visiting relatives not to let Lisa be the one to tell them how to get to church. How right he was! I giggle when I remember it. Google Maps now tells me where to go and reroutes me when I make a wrong turn. Another feature of Google Maps is the re-center button. When we swerve away from the highlighted path to see all the places around to visit, the re-center button brings us back to the most direct route.

Sometimes in our quest for help in healthcare, we end up stuck on detours that deplete our already limited energy. We are constantly bombarded by new ideas for cancer-treatment options. We get pulled this way and that trying to determine which ones are right for us. We end up off center, exhausted, and overwhelmed.

Jesus waits for a little flick of our eyes upward to Him. Sometimes looking up is about all we have the energy to do. It is enough. Looking is believing. Looking to Jesus says, "I can't, but You can." Looking to Him hits the re-center button for our hearts, bodies, souls, and minds. We are pulled back into orbit around Jesus as the center of all we do. His energy becomes our energy.

A dear healthcare practitioner of mine once told me that our healthcare is like a constellation in the sky. Constellations change locations with the seasons just as our healthcare needs will change based on life's dynamic circumstances.

Our lives are a series of seasons. You may be a retired grandmother, a momma to young children, or a daddy to teenagers. While our constellations may look different in various seasons of our lives, Jesus is our North Star, and He never changes. We can trust Jesus to guide us perfectly as we navigate cancer's storm.

These twenty-five things you can do at home are only a microscopic snapshot of the galaxies of options available. One way to handle the many alternatives available to us is to pray over them and ask God for the five things you feel are most important to do daily. Then you can allow other options to travel in and out of your days.

Here are the five points of my daily "star" that I prayerfully arrived at in this season of my life:

1. Seek the fullness of God. Hunger for more and more of Jesus.
2. Sleep. What seems best for me is to go to bed around nine thirty and get up at six.

3. Play. I play hide-and-seek with my kids, do puzzles and board games, play ping-pong, have pajama dance parties, and choose to go down the slide at the park.
4. Breathe deeply. I take walks in nature, watch clouds, do yoga, commit to a regular digital Sabbath, and leave my burdens at the cross each night before climbing into bed. When I notice I am holding the weight of the world between my shoulders, I inhale slowly through my abdomen and exhale even more slowly, dropping my shoulders and letting my arms hang in full surrender.
5. Eat nutritiously. This means keeping a 90/10 ratio that has me 90 percent committed to eating according to my Spirit-led diet. The 10 percent is for the dark-chocolate moments of life. This also means drinking pure water. I simply do the best I can in whatever my circumstances are each day.

Seeking first God's kingdom will bring order to any chaos that has accompanied a cancer diagnosis. As we ask the Lord for wisdom, He will give it. We will recognize it as being from Him, because it will bring peace. This peace is not the type the world gives but a heavenly peace that is unshakable in the midst of trial.

Heaven's wisdom produces a fruit-filled life (see James 3:17). This means we can walk with the Spirit's fruit, including gentleness and kindness, even in the midst of life's hard moments. Jesus is the only One who can make that possible!

Jesus, as we look to You for help, we will be radiant with joy! Amen.

The Palace Beautiful

n February 2017, we received our second "no evidence of disease" MRI result! Since I had been suffering from an adrenal crash, chronic fatigue, and migraines, this was an unexpected result and brought tears of relief. I cried while whispering "Thank You" to Jesus over and over.

Jesus is our safe place. He knows our sorrows and catches our tears. His presence is a promise to hold onto when all else is slipping from our reach.

Amy Carmichael writes,

The servants had gone to their homes in the village, the Indian woman who would presently help me had not come yet; the rooms had that forlorn, deserted air that rooms always wear just after their owners have gone, but

I was not lonely. There was something new in the "feel" of the house, familiar, and yet new, and that sense of a light in a dim place, and an infinitely loving, brooding Presence near (but "near" is too distant a word) was an abiding strength.

But I know it is not the sense of His presence, it is the *fact* of His presence that is our strength and stay. And yet it is comforting when a mother makes some little sign, or speaks some little word to a child who does not see her. And when our Father deals so tenderly with us, then we are very humbly grateful and we store such memories in our heart. And when there is not any feeling we rest on His bare word, "Lo, I am with you always, all the days, and all day long," and are content.[1]

This presence is what filled the Palace Beautiful in John Bunyan's *Pilgrim's Progress*. The version for children, *Little Pilgrim's Progress*, is one of our favorite read-aloud books to our children. It stirs up rich conversation on how to live for the King as we travel toward the Celestial City, our eternal home.

In the book, as Christian is making his journey, just after he makes it past the Hill of Difficulty, he comes upon the Palace Beautiful. He is relieved to be invited to stay for three days. He is nurtured there by Discretion and her daughters, Prudence, Piety, and Charity. Under their care he receives love, protection, rest, and equipping for the rest of his journey.

Our King knows our every need. Often after a Hill of Difficulty, our tired hearts are looking for encouragement, a tight hug, and a day of rest. God has given us His Word to feed our souls. He has given us His Spirit to guide us in every decision, every word, and every step. Sometimes that means choosing to find shelter at a Palace Beautiful. This could mean going "off the radar" for a day to be alone with Jesus to listen. Maybe it's a hike or a long walk with a trusted friend. Maybe it's going to the ocean—as the waves come up, we receive His enduring love, grace, healing, and new strength; as the waves go out, we release to Jesus every weight, every concern, receiving sweet rest for our bodies, hearts, minds, and souls.

The Palace Beautifuls in My Life

Reading about Christian's stay at the Palace Beautiful inspired me to take notice of the godly hearts the Lord has surrounded me with. These Palace Beautifuls have been safe places for my tired heart to rest and receive encouragement from the Scriptures. The richness of our time together has been recorded in my journals. The written experiences allow me to return to graze on the goodness of God found on those worn journal pages.

A Palace Beautiful doesn't have to be a physical location; it can be a phone call across the country. I have two precious hearts who live three thousand miles away from me. Both are Spirit-filled kingdom growers who are available to pray and encourage me from the Scriptures.

We have a dear friend who is eighty-two years old who studies the Scriptures daily. His love for Jesus is contagious. He teaches me more about our triune God, stirring my desire to go deeper into Scripture in my early morning time with Jesus. His messages and phone calls remind me that there are countless hidden gems to keep digging for in God's Word.

This man prays throughout the day for my family, naming each of my children by name. Oh, how precious it is to know we are being prayed over to an all-powerful God! Time spent with him is a taste of the kingdom feast to come. He gifts me with a listening ear to hear the things the Spirit teaches me through Scripture. He encourages me when I am in times of testing. Once he told me he was going to break a leg from jumping for joy in anticipation of the return of Jesus! Oh, how my soul resonates with this joy! The Spirit in me leaps in recognition of the Spirit in him.

I cannot wait for this man to meet my dear grandpa, who has been enjoying the presence of Jesus now for more than eight years. My grandpa was a Palace Beautiful. What a privilege it was to live in his home for a year after I graduated from college. He would sit in his recliner with his Bible while I sat on the couch next to him with mine. I would ask him question after question as we turned the pages of God's Word together. It's been eighteen years since then. That year with my grandpa in the Scriptures remains one of my most formative spiritual years.

I met a Palace Beautiful through a local Bible study I attended. I often ended up on her couch with my feet curled up as if I were a kid in her family. We had tea while she listened to my Lisa thoughts that had built up within, desperate for a place to land. We would talk about the Bible and other books I'd been reading. This precious heart showed me what listening looked like with her attention, questions, and smiles. I am thankful for her friendship that will last into eternity.

God brought another Palace Beautiful into my life during the fall of 2016. Radiant joy overflows from this couple. They put feet to faith, showing me what it looks like to live the victorious life through Jesus Christ. Trials pepper their path to the Celestial City. Through the filling and empowering of the Holy Spirit, they tread hill after hill of difficulty. They sing while they travel of God's goodness, power, and faithfulness. Their lives have been a testimony to the sustaining grace of our triune God. When I read e-mails from them or have the opportunity to see them in person, I am strengthened in my faith. My spirit soars. I am led out with joy and peace. My view is placed back on the cross and eternity to come. Oh to *be* what they have been to me, a Spirit-filled and Spirit-empowered haven for other weary travelers.

Cultivating a Palace Beautiful Heart

If you have put your faith in Jesus Christ, His Spirit resides in your heart. The Spirit is not a vague breeze; He is a co-equal Person of the Godhead. He *is* God. His transforming power cultivates within us a Palace Beautiful environment. Our hearts become a Spirit-filled temple in which He resides, influencing the atmosphere of our home. His presence is palpable in churches in which each heart has taken the time to tune in to their union with the Spirit before entering the sanctuary. It is no different when I walk into a home of hearts that hunger for our triune God. The evidence of the Spirit is breathable.

God's Spirit will invade our hearts when we ask Him to. It is God who draws us to Himself and plants within us this hunger for Him that results in more and more of His Spirit, who continues to fill us as we serve others. We become a safe place for wounded hearts to receive God's love, truth, and grace.

Cultivating a Palace Beautiful environment requires time being immersed in the Scriptures. The Spirit uses the Word of God to show us any sin that needs to be swept out. He creates in us clean hearts and renews right spirits within us (see Ps. 51:10). We thirst to know Him more. We delight in His words.

Meditating on God's Word day and night enables us to be like beautiful fruit-bearing trees (see Ps. 1). We can meditate by reading, writing, praying, memorizing, and pondering the Word of God. We will know God deeper as we study His Word. The more we know Him, the more we love Him. The more we love Him, the more we obey Him out of that love. Serving the Lord is an act of worship that happens from overflow, not overwork. It is our richest privilege to be invited into kingdom work.

Making my home a Palace Beautiful starts with me. As a wife, I am to bring my husband good, not harm, all the days of my life (see Prov. 31:12). The highest good I can bring my husband is a Spirit-filled wife.

As a mother, one of my biggest roles in growing God's kingdom currently is raising up four arrows named Luke, Ellie, Gracie, and Sammy J (see Ps. 127:3–4). One way to sharpen them is through God's Word. First, I must feast on God's Word myself, hiding it in my heart and keeping it readily available for the Spirit to use in my words and actions toward my children. It will show in my kindness and gentleness, which are absent without the work of the Holy Spirit in my heart.

Raising children is kingdom work. I can give my best efforts to teaching them about God and His Word, but it is the Spirit who works to convict and grow them for the King's work. Taking time to pray scriptures over our children is the best gift we can give our kids.

Recently my sister Lynnette and I started a journey through a book of scriptures to pray over our children. We have been writing verses on index cards for their salvation, character, giftings, purposes, and so much more. Having the verses on index cards enables me to take these verses on my walks with me. I love to listen to the wind through the trees while I pray; it reminds me of the Spirit's work in the lives of my children.

After reading the *Safely Home* book by Randy Alcorn, I realized how I have taken for granted the gift of having God's Word at our fingertips:

"As we copy," Quan said, "the words of Yesu are written on our hearts."

"Mother copied it carefully. She would borrow a Bible whenever she could. She'd work for hours by candlelight, praying the words aloud as she copied. I wish I would have listened more closely. Often she would rest her head on Shengjing [the Bible]. Sometimes she would giggle with delight. It was a labor of love. Months, even a year went by when she had no Bible before she died. Mother finished copying Shengjing's final book. A leather worker in church bound it for her."

Ben flipped through the pages. "It's been out in the rain."

"No. Always it was carefully covered. Mother bundled it up before going outside. We do the same."

"But the words are smeared in many places," Ben said.

"It was not rain that smeared the words."[2]

Oh, the value it is to have God's Word at our fingertips! I resolved to write my own copy of the Bible, which I hope to finish before I meet Jesus face to Face. Oh, how I pray the overflow of love for Yesu and His words would wet the pages of my Shengjing. To treasure Yesu above all else!

Our True Home

In March 2017, Steve and I took a day trip to the Oregon coast, about an hour's drive from our home in Portland. The hours we spent there with Jesus renewed our hearts, minds, bodies, and souls. During this day trip, we were led into a season of prayer over putting our home up for sale.

Within a few weeks, as our home-equity loan was reaching its maximum, the Lord granted us perfect peace to proceed with the sale. We had moved into our Portland home when Luke was just four years old, Ellie two, and Gracie a baby. We praised Jesus for the gift that it had been for five years! During the four months we took to prepare the home for the market, we asked Jesus to direct our steps to our next home. We lacked His peace in any area we had looked so far.

While our earthly address would be changing, the Lord assured us that He was our Home, our Palace Beautiful. Our eternal, unchanging Home address was found at eternity's shore. Oh, to think often on the vibrant connection between heaven and what goes on here on Earth. Our lives matter. How we spend our little moments matters. And our words matter.

One day heaven and Earth will pass away, and the new earth will be birthed (see Rev. 21:1)! Then God will make His home with us. He will be our God. We will be His people (see Ezek. 37:27)! My soul soars in joyful anticipation of our eternal Palace Beautiful—Jesus, our forever Home.

The Palace Beautiful psalm below brings awareness to the loveliness and light of our Lord residing in our hearts. May that light of our Jesus in us beckon to all who are lost and seeking shelter from this world of increasing chaos and darkness:

> How lovely is your dwelling place, O LORD of hosts! My soul longs, yes, faints for the courts of the LORD; my heart and flesh sing for joy to the living God.
>
> Even the sparrow finds a home, and the swallow a nest for herself, where she may lay her young, at your altars, O LORD of hosts, my King and my God. Blessed are those who dwell in your house, ever singing your praise! Selah.
>
> Blessed are those whose strength is in you, in whose heart are the highways to Zion. As they go through the Valley of Baca they make it a place of springs; the early rain also covers it with pools. They go from strength to strength; each one appears before God in Zion.
>
> O LORD God of hosts, hear my prayer; give ear, O God of Jacob! Selah. Behold our shield, O God; look on the face of your anointed!
>
> For a day in your courts is better than a thousand elsewhere. I would rather be a doorkeeper in the house of my

God than dwell in the tents of wickedness. For the LORD God is a sun and shield; the LORD bestows favor and honor. No good thing does he withhold from those who walk uprightly. O LORD of hosts, blessed is the one who trusts in you! (Ps. 84)

Thorns of Grace

Despite advances in modern medicine, countless people still suffer from unresolved pain and chronic disease. Questions swirl like funnel clouds when medical mysteries antagonize us. *How did this happen? Why can't anyone help me? Who do I listen to? Will this ever go away?*

The apostle Paul journeyed through antagonistic hardship that remained after pleading for freedom:

> To keep me from becoming conceited because of the surpassing greatness of the revelations, a thorn was given me in the flesh, a messenger of Satan to harass me, to keep me from becoming conceited. Three times I pleaded with the Lord about this, that it should leave me. (2 Cor. 12:7–8)

Countless theologians have contemplated the identity of Paul's thorn. Regardless of what that thorn was, we can connect with the weariness that settles in from the relentless pokes. If not from physical difficulty, maybe the persistent pricks come from a relational conflict, an emotional hole, or a financial hardship. Perhaps our thorn is a prayer that has been answered "not yet" as years keep ticking by. Whatever the name of our thorn, God promises sufficient grace for every hour that passes that it's not removed:

> He said to me, "My grace is sufficient for you, for my power is made perfect in weakness." Therefore I will boast all the more gladly of my weaknesses, so that the power of Christ may rest upon me. For the sake of Christ, then, I am content with weaknesses, insults, hardships, persecutions, and calamities. For when I am weak, then I am strong. (2 Cor. 12:9–10)

Sustaining Grace Versus Delivering Grace

What do we do when the thorn stays? Paul says the answer is grace. In his hymn "Amazing Grace," John Newton mentions two kinds of grace: "'Twas grace that taught my heart to fear [grace that saved him] . . . and grace will lead me home." It is by grace that we are saved and by grace that we are sustained. The Israelites were sustained by God's grace for forty years in the desert. Their sandals didn't wear out!

Each morning we receive our sustaining grace, a daily allowance of oil and flour from Jesus for our day. We never know how much it will be, only that it will be enough. This comes from my favorite biblical example of sustaining grace, found in 1 Kings

17:8–16. The widow of Zarephath always had just enough oil and flour for her day, nothing more.

After receiving our daily flour and oil, we then follow in the footsteps of the little boy who gave his whole lunch to Jesus (see John 6:9–11). Such a little lunch this was to feed thousands! Yet it was enough—because Jesus is always enough. The daily oil and flour He gives us will always be enough for what God has called us to give to Him each day.

We learn about another widow in Luke 21:1–4: "While Jesus was in the Temple, he watched the rich people dropping their gifts in the collection box. Then a poor widow came by and dropped in two small coins. 'I tell you the truth,' Jesus said, 'this poor widow has given more than all the rest of them. For they have given a tiny part of their surplus, but she, poor as she is, has given everything she has'" (NLT).

The widow of Zarephath taught me that Jesus always gives us what we need for each day. The second widow taught me to give Him back everything I have received. No matter how small our daily "lunch" offering may seem, when we offer it to Jesus, He may just feed the multitudes.

The Call to Move

In June 2017, the Lord asked us to offer our lunch to Him: we were invited by Hope4Cancer to come to San Diego to join other patients in filming a story of hope. We were thrilled to have an opportunity to share how Jesus had provided in miraculous ways!

On the filming day on June 12, the Lord did the unexpected. He called Steve and me to move to Southern California! Steve and I sat out on the balcony of our hotel overlooking the water, taking turns sharing how the Holy Spirit had impressed the same call on both of us that morning. It had happened to me during the filming at the same time it had happened to Steve on a shuttle with the children in downtown San Diego! The Holy Spirit had clearly impressed the move on our hearts in the same way God had called Abraham to go out in faith (see Gen. 12:1). We didn't get a bullet-point list of every reason why we were to go. God was asking for our trust and obedience.

We had some doubts as to whether we were physically equipped to make such a big move. We wondered how the children would handle the transition from the Northwest. We grew sober at the thought of moving away from dear friends.

When doubts creep in, God's Word anchors us, reminding us that He is kind and gracious, full of compassion. His Word is filled with stories of His faithful provision. I am excited to one day hear the stories of all the saints in heaven of how God's grace was greater than any circumstance they faced. I can't wait to share my own! There is no higher calling than doing exactly what God has called and equipped us to do for *this* day, knowing that for those who are God's children, the best is always yet to come.

In July 2017, the "For Sale" sign was up. In about three months, the sale of our Portland home was complete. The Lord paid off every medical debt and credit card in one miraculous swoop! He did more than all we could have imagined! Thank You, Jesus!

God's Word Empowers Perseverance

Without the protection God's Word provides, thorns chip away at our perseverance.

I enjoyed frequent scriptural meals with my grandpa, Reverend Mark L. Mitchell, when I lived at his home the year after I graduated from college. An engaging storyteller now in the presence of Jesus, my grandpa's life was marked by perseverance. He received his strength from hours in the Word. I often saw him in his chair in the wee hours of the morning with his Bible warming his lap. Time spent in the Word transferred to a life of perseverance.

Immersing myself in the pages of the Bible that once warmed his lap has been pure delight. Sometimes I bury my nose deep into its tattered pages and deeply inhale. I smile in remembrance of our hours spent discussing Scripture late into the night.

Grandpa fed my hunger for truth. His life of saturation in God's Word spoke to me long after Jesus took him home to heaven. James 1:2–4 teaches that perseverance will finish its work so that we will be mature and complete, not lacking anything. This is a promise, that we will not lack a thing, even in hardship. As we daily immerse ourselves in God's Word, we are equipped with everything we need to stay put under the pressure, resulting in a maturing process in us that allows joy to reach the places that hurt inside.

> Consider it pure joy, my brothers and sisters, whenever you face trials of many kinds, because you know that the testing of your faith produces perseverance. Let perseverance finish its work in you so that you may be mature and complete, not lacking anything. (James 1:2–4, NIV)

My thorns have stirred up an intense hunger for Jesus and His Word. They sharpen my eyes to look for His coming.

The Choice to Bloom

Jeremiah, the weeping prophet, wrote a letter to the exiled Jews during their time of uncertainty, frustration, and disappointment:

> Build houses and settle down; plant gardens and eat what they produce. Marry and have sons and daughters; find wives for your sons and give your daughters in marriage, so that they too may have sons and daughters. Increase in number there; do not decrease. (Jer. 29:5–6, NIV)

What would it have been like to be a Jewish mom of four little ones at the time of the exile? The trek to a foreign land must have plagued her with questions: "Will we be able to stay together? Where are we going? When can we come home? Why is this happening?"

The answer came, "Bloom where you are planted!"

These families were challenged to thrive during their time of captivity rather than fixate on the question "How long, Lord?" (see Jer. 29). Their "thorn" remained, but God's grace enabled them to bloom despite it.

Several times over the last five years, in moments of intense despair, I have felt a pressure on my shoulder while I have heaved tears out. Then came the inner whisper: "'I know the plans I have for you,' declares the LORD, 'plans to prosper you and not to harm you, plans to give you hope and a future'" (Jer. 29:11, NIV). His words quieted me.

God did promise the Jewish exiles that He would bring them back into their homeland, but the timing would be His, and not immediate. The Jewish people were urged to bloom, knowing that God would restore them one day.

Hearing the word "wait" may evoke discomfort and frustration in us. But through the promise of His empowering Spirit, we can bloom in our hard.

When the Thorn Remains

A thorn is an opportunity to show the world how truly precious Jesus is.

Amy Carmichael wrote of roses that bloomed in briers, describing beautiful fruit from the Spirit growing in the places of life:

Thou has not that, My child, but thou hast me,
And am not I alone enough for thee?

I know it all, know how thy heart was set
Upon this joy which is not given yet.

And well I know how through the wistful days
Thou walkest all the dear familiar ways
As unregarded as a breath of air,
But there in love and longing, always there.

I know it all; but from thy brier shall blow
A rose for others, If it were not so
I would have told thee, Come, then, say to Me:
My Lord, my Love, I am content with Thee.[1]

Amy Carmichael knew the "not yet" answer in response to
her pleas to be up from her bed, out of her room, and restored to
the ministry she loved. The last two decades of her life she spent
unable to get out of bed. Yet book after book that she wrote from
her bed is filled with evidence of spiritual intimacy, a love-filled
relationship between her and Jesus. Her life reflects the truth of
Romans 8:38-39:

> I am convinced that nothing can ever separate us from
> God's love. Neither death nor life, neither angels nor de-
> mons, neither our fears for today nor our worries about
> tomorrow—not even the powers of hell can separate us
> from God's love. No power in the sky above or in the
> earth below—indeed, nothing in all creation will ever be
> able to separate us from the love of God that is revealed
> in Christ Jesus our Lord. (NLT)

Through the power of the Spirit in her, Amy made a choice to
love God and others despite her thorn of being bedridden. When
we choose to love the Lord our God with all our hearts, minds,

soul, and strength, His peace begins to pad the sharpness of those thorns we so badly wish were gone.

His grace may deliver us from our thorns here or there, but it will always sustain us. The thorns of grace Jesus has allowed to stay in my life deepen my gratefulness for the suffering He endured for me on the cross and the riches stored up for me in heaven. He is my great Reward!

We do not have to wait a single moment to experience the eternal gift of His companionship. He is the closest Friend we have. We can tell Him all about our pain without even needing to expend the energy to use our voices. He understands every cell in our bodies, every thought zipping through our minds, and every sigh troubling our souls. Oh, how sweet to my soul His friendship is!

When my thorns grow noisy, I love to stare into the ocean waves, the billowing white clouds, the towering mountains, or the star-speckled sky and tell Him all about it. When my pouring out has slowed, He who has waited so patiently for a chance to speak whispers, "Yes, little one, I am here. I am in you. I am with you. I will never leave you. I love you. I hear you, My daughter."

He releases me from the quest to understand every mystery, for the secret things belong to Him (see Deut. 29:29). I lay my tired head down on His back, resting between His shoulders (see Deut. 33:12). His strength stills my worried wiggles. I settle into His rest, releasing a sigh of contentment. I am His, and He is mine. And that is always enough.

To Live Is Christ

n the beginning God was the composer and champion of light and life: "In the beginning, God created the heavens and the earth. The earth was without form and void, and darkness was over the face of the deep. And the Spirit of God was hovering over the face of the waters" (Gen. 1:1–2). God spoke light over the face of the deep. Seas were gathered, and land appeared. God filled the land with vibrant life from plants to animals to humans. He called it good. And it was, until sin entered in with Eve's bite of forbidden fruit. Black paint marred God's brilliant masterpiece. Pain, sickness, and disease darkened our world.

In His loving-kindness God did not leave us lost in endless night to live in constant separation from Himself. He sent His only Son, Jesus, to light up our darkness. In Him is life, and that life is the light of men. "The light shines in the darkness, and the darkness has not overcome it" (John 1:5). We are all walking in the valley of the shadow of death. Jesus came to shine a light into our valley, and He walks every step with us. He rescued us from the kingdom of darkness and brought us into the kingdom of light (see Col. 1:13)!

My cancer diagnosis awakened in me a deeper hunger for Jesus, for all of Him. My life verse became Philippians 1:21: "To me, to live is Christ and to die is gain" (NIV).

The Spirit of God who hovered over those dark waters at creation is ready to fill every cell of our body with Himself. Nothing can overcome the light and love of Jesus living in us. Nothing. When we become one with Jesus, His light in us makes us the most radiant people on the planet. "To live is Christ" means a life empowered by the Holy Spirit. We have the same power that rose Jesus from the dead at work within us. Amy Carmichael reminded me that "the powers of the Eternal are not bound between the covers of this Book [the Bible]."[1]

"To live is Christ" is to live a life free from sin's power over us. Every victory we experience on Earth is because of Jesus in us! "For we died and were buried with Christ by baptism. And just as Christ was raised from the dead by the glorious power of the Father, now we also may live new lives" (Rom. 6:4, NLT). Because our old sinful selves were crucified with Christ, sin has lost its power in our lives! Because we died with Christ, we will also live with Him (see Rom. 6:6–8). When Christ, who is our life, is revealed to the whole world, we will share in all His glory (see Col. 3:2–4). By faith in Christ we are brought into this place of undeserved privilege where we now stand, and we confidently and joyfully look forward to sharing God's glory (see Rom. 5:2)!

Created to Do Good

Despite sin's marring effect, God planned good things long ago for us to do, and waves of hardship don't erode that: "We are

God's masterpiece. He has created us anew in Christ Jesus, so we can do the good things he planned for us long ago" (Eph. 2:10, NLT). These good things do not earn us salvation, which is a gift by grace alone, nor do they increase God's love for us. They are simply the overflow from hearts that are flooded by His love.

During an especially debilitating portion of my cancer journey, I cried out into the Pacific Northwest rain, "Look at the mess I am! Jesus, what good can I possibly be doing?" Our infinitely compassionate Father reminded me that He looked at my heart, not the tasks I could or couldn't do. The breath of His Spirit in my lungs was evidence that He still wanted to do something good through me.

He will never call us to something He won't help us complete through the indwelling of His Spirit. Joy abounds with our simple "Yes, Lord!" Hardships highlight our complete inability to function without God's constant upholding. I resonate with Brother Lawrence: "Lord, I cannot do this, unless thou enablest me."[2]

"I have been crucified with Christ. It is no longer I who live, but Christ who lives in me. And the life I now live in the flesh I live by faith in the Son of God, who loved me and gave himself for me" (Gal. 2:20). Christ in us is the Word in us. When we pray, "Lord, take full possession of me," we walk in complete union with Christ, bearing the fruits of the Spirit. Because the Spirit fully controls us, we can be love, because He is love. We can be kind, because He is kind. We *can* because *He* can.

The Spirit of Christ propels us forward into this dark world as living letters of the Word of God. May He write on us His salvation, redemption, holiness. When others see us, may they read only of Him.

Strengthened at the King's Table

It is dining at the King's table that fills us to overflowing to be Jesus for others. This is what "to live is Christ" means. His nourishing

Word lifts our sadness. His arms hold our tired hearts. The King's love pulls us into Himself as we sit with Him. While we are feasting with Him at the table, He tends to our wounds. He restores, renews, reveals, assigns, and equips.

Sadly, sometimes sin stings my soul. An inner room in the deepest part of me basks in the sweet closeness of Jesus, but when I allow sin to sneak in, it settles like dust, forming webs that tangle me up. I become distanced from Him. I begin to avoid the table my King has set for me. I glance over to see the beautifully arranged table setting, complete with a name card saving my spot. He will never force us to come or to stay. He simply pulls out a chair and pats it as He whispers, "I'm here. I'm ready. I'd love your company." His love awaits us.

"To live is Christ" means we are partakers, not performers. Holiness isn't work to be done but a Person to partake of. The Person is Jesus. One way to partake of Him is to spend time in Scripture getting to know His promises.

Standing on God's promises rather than our emotions protects us from our own perceptions. The Word of God transforms us, inspires power, gives us hunger for all of God until we "live and move in the atmosphere of holiness."[3]

"To live is Christ" means we walk life's rocky paths with sure-footed confidence in God's Word. God said it; we believe it. He said it; we obey it. Feasting at our King's table enables us to live as Christ for others. Our oneness with Him will enable us to live courageously in His power, free from fear and the enslavement of sin, bearing fruit in all seasons—the truly abundant life!

To Die Is Gain

We are all going to die. I may die from cancer. I may be hit by a bus. I may die in an earthquake or from old age. But unless Jesus returns first, I *will* experience an earthly death. So will you.

For believers in Jesus Christ, perhaps a greater question than "How will I die?" is "How will I live?" Each day that God fills our bodies with His breath is a day for us to live as Christ for others. When Jesus brings us home to heaven, it will be gain. "For to me to live is Christ, and to die is gain" (Phil. 1:21)! As a dear pastor of mine says, as Christians, we are in a *win-win* situation!

Jesus is the upholder of our lives and the One who will one day bring us safely home. Jesus is the way. Jesus is the truth. Jesus is life. Jesus is light. He resides in us as light that shines in the darkness, "and the darkness has not overcome it" (John 1:5)!

Jesus came to be our peace (see Eph. 2:14). He came to set us free from being enslaved by the fear of death (see Heb. 2:15). This is good news! We are set free from the fear of death. We are equipped to live as the light and love of Jesus to a world that is desperate to be cured from terminal sadness. Jesus is that cure.

Comfort warms my innermost being when my eyes fasten on the cross, removing any taste of doubt regarding God's love for me. Looking upon the cross reminds me that for Christians, any form of suffering is temporary. A spotless Lamb, God's only Son, was crucified on a cross as payment for my sin and for yours. God, the perfect Father, turned His back on His only Son so that He would never have to turn His back on us. Jesus set us free from the wages of our sin. He took our rightful punishment and declared it paid in full. An endless ocean of grace, joy, and forever love replaced eternal separation from God. When Jesus climbed on that cross and spread His arms out, He never put them down. They are still open as He waits. He longs for our leaning hard into Him.

I have known Jesus since I was a young child. But today I am one with Him. When I walk with complete awareness of my union with Jesus, I am not afraid, because He is not afraid. I have hope because He is hope. I have peace because He is peace—peace that stands strong amidst life's mysteries.

Unsinkable hope offsets the tears we shed in seasons of pain. Jesus, our gentle Shepherd, is ready to fold us into the safety of His arms. As we graze in the green pastures of His Word, we will be strengthened by rich soul food, enabling us to "go out in joy and be led forth in peace" (Isa. 55:12).

Because of Jesus, we are winners in life and winners in death. The best is always yet to come! One day our wheels will touch down in eternity. What an amazing homecoming that will be! Our faith will become sight. Faith is being certain of what we do not see (see Heb. 11:1). I am certain of Jesus Christ, the Son of the living God. I am certain He deeply loves me, died for me, rose again, and reigns victorious over sin and death. I am certain that He will reward those who earnestly seek Him (see Heb. 11:6).

Jesus Himself is my great Reward. That makes dying gain. We get to enjoy Him forever. Thinking on our death will change how we live. I don't want to waste a moment of the days God has numbered for me. The recurring plea of my soul remains, "Precious Jesus, don't let me waste my life!" Serving Him here is a privilege that will expire. We are His body. We represent the kingdom of light! We are a channel of His love. I have this one vapor of a moment to sing of His beauty, love, and light that will triumph into eternity.

I love to imagine sliding into our heavenly home plate having nothing left to give! Jesus will have upheld my life to its intended completion. I will look up into His beautiful gentle eyes and meet the truest of Love.

What If It's True?

The question "What if . . . ?" frequently invades my mind. These "what if" questions have been present in my life as long as I can remember. What if I don't make the team? What if I trip going on-stage? What if the plane crashes? What if my baby stops breathing?

What if my child gets cancer? What if I get cancer? What if treatment fails?

But we can turn our "what ifs" into positive questions! What if I do make the team? What if it's the best basketball season yet? What if the traffic keeps me from an accident? What if cancer ends up freeing me from anxiety? What if my journey with cancer gifts me new or deeper relationships? What if hurts in my life open up more of heaven's view? What if health struggles keep me snuggling my children more and sweeping floors less?

And to those who have declared God not real or a far-off someone not actively shaping our moments—what if God *is* real? What if Jesus is God's Son? What if He is fully engaged in directing our lives?

Before God created the world, He enjoyed a perfect, delight-filled love relationship as a triune God. Yahweh—I AM, "My Being from My Being." Timeless existence. Yahweh, one God in three distinct Persons, all glorifying one another.

Then God spoke the universe into existence from the atom to the galaxies to the first humans. Adam and Eve enjoyed living in the beautiful garden of Eden and taking walks with God. But a bite of the forbidden fruit birthed sin into the world. God and man, once in perfect fellowship, were now separated by sin.

God created us to be with Him. After Adam and Eve sinned, God could have destroyed everything and started over. Not our loving God. He chose to make a way to fix the broken relationship through His Son, Jesus Christ. Fully God and fully man, Jesus lived the sinless life required to become the perfect Lamb sacrifice.

Precious hearts, *what if it's true?* What if the blood He shed on the cross that day was for me? For you?

I could tell you that more than five hundred witnesses saw Jesus after He rose again. We could dive into all the prophecies in the Scriptures that have been fulfilled. But faith is not by might nor by power but by God's Spirit (see Zech. 4:6).

It's God's hand that stirs. It's His whisper through which we hear, "It's true!"

It's true that "God so loved the world that he gave his one and only Son, that whoever believes in him shall not perish but have eternal life" (John 3:16, NIV). It's true that Jesus is the way, the truth, and the life (see John 14:6). It's true that He is the equipping through all life's bumps. It's true that *He is* life eternal!

Our Invitation

We have each received this invitation from God:

> Do you believe that I created you to be with Me? Do you believe that our relationship is broken by your sin? Do you believe that the death and resurrection of My only Son, Jesus, stamped out death with paid in full?
>
> Circle yes or no.

When we circle yes on that invitation, we get to start that relationship with Jesus right away! We receive His free gift of eternal life. Death loses its sting. We grieve, but we grieve with hope as the earthly good-byes for those in God's forever family become "See you soon."

One day Jesus will terminate all evil, and that includes cancer. We will enter into a tearless life forevermore, "for this light momentary affliction is preparing for us an eternal weight of glory beyond all comparison" (2 Cor. 4:17). We will drink the cup of glory that washes down all Earth's sorrows.

I quake in anticipation of that moment when He will reach out His Savior hands and say, "*Enough!*" Cancer will flee. Disease will be gone. Limbs will be restored. Those bound in wheelchairs will rise up and run. There will no longer be any sorrow or sighing. The great reunion will begin.

Life isn't about longevity. It's about influence. Until Jesus calls me home to heaven, I have another moment, another day, another year to display the beauty and value of Jesus Christ to a world that is groaning under the weight of despair. We, the body of Christ, are the hope people are looking for. Christ in us, the hope of glory!

My hope is your hope. Precious hearts, your RSVP awaits.

Believe today that Jesus saves. It is because of Jesus that I can say, "For me to live is Christ, and to die is gain!"

Will your death be gain?

I know that through your prayers and God's provision of the Spirit of Jesus Christ what has happened to me will turn out for my deliverance. I eagerly expect and hope that I will in no way be ashamed but will have sufficient courage so that now as always Christ will be exalted in my body, whether by life or death. For to me, to live is Christ and to die is gain. (Phil. 1:19–21, NIV)

Oh, coming One, do not delay!

Afterword

Our family recently began our second year in California. I smile thinking of the hours my sister Lynnette and I have shared side by side with our pink and green Bibles, sneaking in quiet moments together as our children have played. Another gift has been my deepening friendship with a sister in Christ who lives about an hour away. When Jesus brings us together, the Spirit in me leaps with joy in recognition of the Spirit in her. Her eyes speak of deep and true love for Jesus. She has taught me by example how to pray big and trust always.

When the Lord called Steve and me to Southern California, we had no details; we had only the words "trust and obey." I have now had two years without any evidence of disease showing up on imaging. I continue to struggle with various chronic health issues for which God's answer for healing has been "Not yet." In accordance with the widow of Luke 18, I will persist in my asking. I will trust the heart of my Father in the waiting.

Through prayer, Steve and I decide which health treatments I will continue doing and which ones we can let go for a season. We remain on a modified home program from Hope4Cancer and will continue in the future with periodic imaging and labs to monitor my status.

Another blessing that came from our move to California has been a local chiropractor whom I connect well with. I look forward not just to the chiropractic adjustments but the camaraderie we share in our view of wellness that sparks energizing conversations.

In January 2018, the Lord gave me the word "quiet." In times of uncertainty throughout this year, the Spirit has gently asked me to wait on the Lord over and over again. As a society, we have been deconditioned to the discipline of waiting in our modern-day culture of "instant" everything. Yet it is through waiting that each of us receives the peaceful assurance from Jesus for the next steps we should take.

These steps will be unique to our individual callings, and we must walk courageously through the grace and strength of the Spirit within us, even when He leads us on a path no one else has been asked to take. My observation of the Bible is that it's filled with courageous risk takers who were simply filled with the Spirit. I am sure the disciples must have thought Peter was nuts for getting out of the boat to walk on water.

Cancer tempted me to become a prisoner of fear rather than a prisoner of hope. Recently the Holy Spirit, my whisper within, gently nudged me to renew some life goals I had made years ago that faded out of sight when cancer grew and my view of the future shrank. Today I choose to live well. I choose to say yes to Jesus and no to fear. Yes to using my spiritual gifts today. Yes to understanding that every circumstance I face is a sovereign appointment and an opportunity. I choose to pray big, pray hard, and pray through.

Disease can steal vision, and chronic pain clouds long-term hopes. Yet every child of God has authority in the name of Jesus to take back the ground where the enemy has been breathing lies, sprouting weeds, and choking fruit. The Spirit empowers us to be the aroma of Jesus Christ even when our prayers for complete healing are answered "Not yet" today.

By connecting to the Spirit within us, we can see both near and far. The Spirit shows us how to use our spiritual gifts to live out our unique assignments here on Earth. Our good Father has a special way with each of His children, and all of us have access to His yes for every promise made in Scripture. Our circumstances will be different, but our mission is the same: to seek and save the lost.

Our aim as believers is to study the life of Jesus and imitate Him in all we do. Jesus was peace, hope, and compassion. Jesus tended to the wounded hearts. Jesus spoke to the crowds, but He also pursued the one. He wants us to do the same. We are His peace, hope, and compassion to our spouses, our children, a friend, a fellow patient. He may call us to speak a Word of encouragement from Scripture to one wounded heart or a stadium of forty-five thousand people. He decides who and when; we simply give Him our "Yes, Lord."

In March 2018, Steve's and my hearts were stirred to pray for revival, for an awakening to the beauty of Jesus. He began with *us*.

The Holy Spirit is nearer than our breath. His power is at work within us to bring to completion every good work the Lord will call us to. His voice has become truth and light for everything Steve and I do. He has consistently asked us to let go of plans and trust Him. He sprung up in us an intense fervor to rekindle the art of listening—to sit and look into the eyes of those speaking to us with no screen between us, to give our children the gift of our attention. He has taught us to start every day on our knees adoring Him, thanking Him, and praying *big* prayers. We are His children. He is for us, not against us. His love is tender, nurturing, affectionate, and unconditional.

May His love awaken us to the power and presence of His Spirit within us. May we go forth and be the love this world is hungry for.

Notes

Chapter 1: Fear Factor: The Diagnosis
1. Amy Carmichael, "God of the Stars," *Mountain Breezes: The Collected Poems of Amy Carmichael* (Fort Washington, PA: CLC, 2000), 15.

Chapter 2: First Waves: Seeking the Cure
1. Henry Frost, *Miraculous Healing: Why Does God Heal Some and Not Others?* (Tain, Ross-shire, Scotland: Christian Heritage, 2008), 99.
2. WebMD, "Follicular Lymphoma," www.webmd.com/cancer/lymphoma/follicular-lymphoma#1 (accessed August 3, 2018).

Chapter 4: Man's Wisdom
1. The Fish Family Name Game gives people a chance to call into Portland's radio channel The Fish and share about a special child who has the same name the radio channel picks for that day. See The Fish, "Fish Family Name Game," http://thefish-portland.com/content/all/fish-family-name-game (accessed August 6, 2018).
2. Matthew Henry, *Matthew Henry's Concise Commentary on the Whole Bible* (Nashville: Thomas Nelson, 1997), 582.

Chapter 6: When the Teacher Is Quiet
1. F. B. Meyer, *John the Baptist* in *Living the Christ Life* (Fort Washington, PA: CLC, 2009),
2. *Adventures in U.S. History* (Rolla, MO: My Father's World, 2015), 50.

Chapter 7: Happiness
1. Michel de Montaigne, Goodreads, www.goodreads.com/quotes/6751782-my-life-has-been-full-of-terrible-misfortunes-most-of (accessed July 30, 2018).

Chapter 8: Change the Terrain
1. A. W. Tozer, *The Crucified Life: How to Live Out a Deeper Christian Experience* (Bloomington, MN: Bethany, 2014), 170–75.

Chapter 11: When Life Tastes Like Gravel: Seasons of Lament
1. C. S. Lewis, *The Horse and His Boy* (New York: HarperCollins, 1994), 162.
2. Ibid., 163.
3. Lindsay Terry, "Story Behind the Song: What a Friend We Have in Jesus," staugustine.com, April 23, 2015, www.staugustine.com/living/religion/2015-04-23/story-behind-song-what-friend-we-have-jesus (accessed August 7, 2018).
4. Ibid.

Chapter 12: Cancer and My Littles
1. Ann Voskamp, Facebook post, June 14, 2016, www.facebook.com/AnnVoskamp/photos/pb.324577877554393.-2207520000.1466205957./1238130919532413/?-type=3 (accessed September 24, 2018).
2. Christoph Von Schmid, *The Bird's Nest* (Mount Morris, NY: Lamplighter, 2002), footnote, 27–28.

Chapter 13: Kinetic Love
1. Brennan Manning, *The Furious Longing of God* (Colorado Springs: Cook, 2009), 29–40.
2. Helen L. Taylor, *Little Pilgrim's Progress: From John Bunyan's Classic* (Chicago: Moody, 2006), 314.
3. Carmichael, "Love Through Me," *Toward Jerusalem* (Fort Washington, PA: CLC, 1961), 11.

Chapter 14: In My Medicine Cabinet
1. "What Is Structured Water?" Structured Water, www.structuredwaterunit.com/articles/structuredwater/what-is-structured-water (accessed August 10, 2018).

Chapter 15: The Palace Beautiful
1. Carmichael, *Gold by Moonlight* (Fort Washington, PA: CLC, 2017), 94.
2. Randy Alcorn, *Safely Home* (Carol Stream, IL: Tyndale, 2011), 129.

Chapter 16: Thorns of Grace
1. Carmichael, "A Song While We Wait," *Rose from Brier* (Fort Washington, PA: CLC, 2015), 52.

Chapter 17: To Live Is Christ
1. Carmichael, *Gold by Moonlight*, 78.
2. Brother Lawrence, *The Practice of the Presence of God: The Best Rule of a Holy Life* (New York: Revell, 1895), 10.
3. Smith Wigglesworth, *Smith Wigglesworth on Prayer: A 30-Day Devotional* (Lake Mary, FL: Creation House, 1997), 12.